Label Me

My Journey Towards an Autism Diagnosis

Francesca Baird

Review of *Label Me*

Books written by autistic people about their lives are rare, and particularly those written by women, but of those, very few are as open and honest as Francesca Baird is, in *Label Me*.

From the very first line I was gripped by her story, and could barely tear myself away, I was so desperate to find out what happened next.

Francesca's story is harrowing and at times, difficult to read, but sadly not that uncommon in autistic females, many of whom find that their lives spiral out of control resulting in long term hospital stays, when, overwhelmed by outside stimuli (known as sensory overload), and an inability to control external events, life becomes too much for them, resulting in 'autism burnout', depression, and for some, more serious mental health problems.

Happily, Francesca, after hitting rock bottom, bounced back, and though her life is still difficult, she has found ways in which to live, work and negotiate her way through the neurotypical world.

What sets this book apart from most other accounts by autistic people, is that Francesca takes us with her on her journey from a childhood filled with anxiety and fear, through an adolescence of 'masking' in order to fit in at school, work, and social events, on, in to her early 20s, when consumed by an obsession with an older man, she almost destroyed herself; to motherhood, job security, and finally, the autism label that answered her questions, all whilst giving us an insight into the innermost workings, of an autistic mind.

Francesca's ability to reflect on and articulate her innermost feelings during periods of crisis, as well as her accounts of what everyday life is like for those on 'The Spectrum' make this a 'must read' book for newly diagnosed adults, parents, other family members, carers and autism professionals. But I warn you! Once you pick it up, you won't be able to put it down!

Margaret Hodder, Chair, Grampian Autistic Society

Acknowledgements

I would like to thank the following people for supporting my crowd-funding campaign and for making this book possible:

Alistair Baird, Cara Baird, The Creative Fund by Backer Kit team, Louise Morris, Michael W, Doreen Baird, Chris Morris, Kathryn Morris, CTMoeller, David, Pat Byrne, Gavin Boyter, Maggie Morris, Sarah Thornton, Christine Black, Matt H, Richard McMellon, Ben Bullough, Catherine Aitken, Pat, Callum Walls, Anna Cross, David McCarthy, Alison Hamilton, James Baird, Jess, Keith Robertson, Laura Imlach, Anne Dalziel, Dougie Craighead, Scott Dillon, Dyan, Atthis Arts, LLC, Melissa Burke, Christopher Xavier Lozano, Emi, Linda Mary Wagner, John-Paul Broughton, Hamilton Huxham, Yvonne Burney, Claire Bester, Michael McLeod, Victoria Murdoch, Hazel Farquhar, Carole Jackman, Austin VanderWeide, Kristen Dyrr, Fiona Black, Christopher Collingridge, Daniel Klein, Peter Curievici, Christopher, Antony Balbier, Cathy Lynch, Douglas Cid, Frances Gilroy, Elizabeth Gilroy, Lucinda Tanner, Jane Little, Alison Hamilton, Joyce Stewart.

I would also like to thank Hugh Barker, my editor, for his invaluable contribution.

Finally, I would like to thank Simon Avery for the cover design and Peter Davis for the internal layout.

For Oscar Forbes

Contents

Foreword

John Forrester, Specialist Autism Consultant

Since the word was first used as a diagnostic term in the 1940s, our understanding of autism has evolved and changed. The concept of an autism spectrum has been part of a broadening of the definition, allowing diagnosticians and others to open-mindedly review the developmental history and patterns of cognitive, behavioural and sensory difference experienced by approximately 1 in 100 people. Clinicians now recognise neurodevelopmental differences and may ultimately provide a diagnosis that can accurately place a patient on the autism spectrum. The prevalence of autism is not likely to have increased, but our understanding of differences experienced by people has improved.

In recent years, the developing awareness of autism in females has perhaps been of particular significance, as it has led to a revision of the longstanding belief that the condition predominantly affected males. Although particular and of course unique, Francesca's story reflects the experience of many girls and women who have struggled at times: socially, emotionally and in other ways. From the outset, this book is an example of Francesca's unguarded candour, her honesty and her sense of humour: but meanwhile there is a story of emotional distress and difficulties in relating to the neurotypical world.

Intelligent and courageous, Francesca's memoir can be read without an interest in autism, but some readers might identify with and relate to aspects of her experience: sometimes with a smile, and often with affection. I love the title of Francesca's book: it is testimony to the importance of recognizing differences characteristic of the autism spectrum, as well as the validation and self-development that recognition and diagnosis promotes.

Label Me

My Journey Towards an Autism Diagnosis

Avoiding Reality

I have just lost £16,000 in two days! I feel nauseous, anxious, and confused. I was up £8,000 just a couple of days ago. *How did I manage to lose so much money, and so quickly? I had identified a money-making strategy that worked – cut your losses and run with the gains! Such a simple set of rules! Why didn't I follow them?*

I ponder this for a moment before settling on the only possible explanation: poor decision making brought on by a fear: a fear of being out of control. I had to find a way to relieve the anxiety, to take back control. Spread betting is not only my comfort stimulus, but it also offers a way out: a form of escapism from real life. With one finger tapping on my phone, and the other picking my now bleeding lips, I consider the outcome of my actions.

How will I ever pay off my debts? It will take months… years! I can't tell my parents: I can't tell anyone. They will think that I am a failure: I am a failure.

I am lying in bed, crippled with anxiety and unable to move. Face down on my pillow, I am trying to hide the tears from my son, but it is futile. He can sense my anguish and is desperately trying to relieve me of it. "Mum, are you okay? Why are you crying? It will be okay."

I am breathless and unable to speak. The initial shock and repetitive questioning is quickly replaced by a sombre mood and then depression. I am mentally and physically exhausted: desperate to escape everything and everyone. Overcome by emotion, I have a strong desire to curl up in a ball and sleep for eternity.

Six Months Later

Well…here I am. Sitting in Costa Coffee, devouring caramel short-bread and buzzing from the effects of my small Americano with semi-skimmed milk on the side. Costa – my haven and comfort place – is where I go to procrastinate and consider my goals and ambitions. Today is no different. I have the same repetitive thoughts whizzing through my head. *Can I be in a successful long-term relationship? How do I become a millionaire? Can I develop feelings for someone who is actually available? Do I even want to be in a relationship?*

Despite my best efforts to search for an answer to these elusive questions, I invariably fail to reach a sensible, logical conclusion. This is my life, this is me… in a constant state of anxiety, desperately trying to create structure and meaning as I navigate my way through this unpredictable, precarious thing we call life.

I would say I had a relatively "normal" upbringing. I put quotation marks around the word "normal" for two reasons. Firstly, how do we define normality? Does it lie within the realm of cultural norms and societal pressure to conform to these norms? If so, the definition of normality will inevitably differ across cultures, groups of people and even between individuals. Secondly, being raised by an eccentric and somewhat deviant mother, many would argue that my family upbringing was far from what is deemed as normal… I will let you be the judge of that.

I was fortunate enough to be brought up by two loving parents (Doreen and Alistair) in our family home with my three siblings and our wonderful border collie, Linda. I have two older sisters, Cara and Louise. Cara – who is only a couple of years older than me – is, and always has been, level-headed, strong-willed and independent. She is also family-orientated and extremely loyal – the type of person you would want to have around in a crisis. At one point in our childhood, Cara and I had adjoining bedrooms. She had a pink carpet and a wardrobe full of Barbies. By contrast, I had a green carpet and a wardrobe stuffed with Ninja Turtles and characters from *Star Wars*. This is testimony to how different we were… although it didn't seem to matter, as we were still close.

My sister Louise is eight years older than me and, at times, she represented more of a mother figure than a sibling. She was always very open and I loved hearing about her crazy antics the day after she had had a night out. Her zest for life was infectious and, whenever I was with her, all my anxieties evaporated. Until recently, I had a collection of items Louise had been given by former boyfriends over the years (like a shrine). I think I lost them when I moved to a new house a couple of years ago.

I shared similar interests with my younger brother James. There are only a couple of years between us and we would often spend the weekend together, watching TV, gaming or playing indoor football. On a Saturday evening, we would re-enact scenes from *The Gladiators* by play fighting. It was great fun but usually ended in tears since he was much stronger than me and unwilling to let me win. However, we were and still are very close – as I am with all of my family.

I didn't see much of my older brother Stevie when I was growing up. He got married when I was very young and moved to Australia shortly after. Due to geographical limitations, his visits were infrequent, but each one was special. Despite not seeing him as much I would like to, I enjoy his company and I have always felt at ease with him. I intend to visit him in Australia, but only once I feel strong enough to embrace such a major change to my environment.

My dad – a born communist – strived for peace and equality and avoided confrontation: it used to drive my mum crazy when she was asked to line up with her children to have a family discussion following a heated argument. I think she was looking for his support, for him to irrefutably take her side and discipline their children accordingly. Of course, this rarely happened. Instead, he took on the role of a mediator, giving each person the opportunity to air their grievances, to try to reach a mutual understanding. Thinking about it now, I don't think I have ever heard my dad shout; which is remarkable really since my mum suffered from premenstrual tension when we were young and would fly off the handle for the smallest of reasons.

My mum is – and always has been – impulsive, emotional and fiercely erratic. It seemed like she got bored easily and often created a drama for her own amusement – usually by winding up her children and taunting strangers (more on this later). Despite their differences, my parents somehow managed to compromise, and stay together, to ensure that their children were brought up in a stable environment. However, we did move around a lot (I had lived in seven different houses by the time I was 13 years old), which wasn't easy for me since I don't like change. We regularly went on family holidays and my early life followed the usual, predictable trajectory of attending school, developing friendships, forming romantic relationships (of sorts) and all those things that contribute to the development of a happy, healthy child. On the surface, life was great.

Unknown to family and friends, I was struggling internally. As far back as I can remember, I have been consumed by thoughts of physical illness and death. Even as I am writing these words, I have a feeling of anxiety and the urge to either remove the words from this page or do something to counteract their effects. But what effects? If I die tomorrow, surely it would be coincidental and have nothing to do with the words in this book? Right?

I am being silly and irrational: I know I am! My feet are clenched, and I feel irritable, but for the sake of the book, I am going to put my irrational thoughts aside and carry on typing.

Back to the Start

"I think your family should see a psychologist".

This was a suggestion made by my nursery teacher in response to my unwillingness to speak at school. I could speak… very well in fact. I just chose not to. My friend Stuart, who took me under his wing and looked after me, was more than happy to talk on my behalf. My mum was both shocked and surprised by this alarming suggestion. She knew me better than anyone. If there had been any underlying problems, surely she, of all people, would have detected them. I had no problem communicating with close friends and family outside the school setting. Understandably, she attributed my lack of speech to me being shy. It's not surprising then, that she quickly dismissed the teacher's suggestion that the family should take me to see a professional.

Thinking about it now, it was possibly a combination of social difficulties and the need to control my environment that prevented me from communicating at nursery. As someone who was acutely aware of my surroundings, being in a strange environment with lots of people I didn't know was an overwhelming experience for me. To make matters worse, I had no control over it, and no escape plan for when things got too much. The anxiety triggered by these factors inevitably resulted in me being withdrawn. Instead of interacting and engaging in social play, I chose instead to sit in the corner of the classroom, observing and taking it all in. Perhaps if we had sought help after my teacher's suggestion, things would have been different. Knowing what I know now, I would have been better equipped to face the challenges that were yet to come, and my parents would have been in a better position to support me.

However, I do not feel any sort of resentment towards my family for failing to notice that my brain processes things differently. My parents had to juggle their jobs, raising four children and accommodating two young students who rented the spare rooms in our family home. There was no time for individual problems. Life was a struggle for everyone, and we just had to get on with it the best we could.

I had a couple of social encounters with my teacher outside the school setting. On one occasion, I was in the supermarket with my grandfather. She spotted us before we noticed her, and secretly listened to me rattling on about something I was interested in (probably the *Teenage Mutant Ninja Turtles*). As soon as I finished my piece, she made her presence known with the statement, "Wow! She can speak".

On another, separate occasion, I met my teacher when I was walking down the street with my sister, Louise. After the platitudes ("hi", "how are you?" and all that nonsense), my teacher asked me if I was enjoying the holidays. My response was:

"Do you know Eddie Murphy's favourite saying?"

"No, what is it?"

"Get the fuck outta here!"

Beverly Hills Cop was my favourite film at that time and I probably said it either to make her laugh or to make my interest known. Either way, I think it showed her my humorous side. To be honest, she was probably surprised that I responded at all.

I don't have many memories of my early schooling. I have been told that I was quiet and well behaved in the classroom. I do however recall the journey home from school, or rather my experience with the lollipop woman who was stationed near where I lived. As my house was on the same street as my school, my mum had decided it was close enough for me to walk home by myself – at least part of the way. However, our house was on the opposite side of the street from the school and I was too young to cross the road myself. I had two options: walk to the end of street and accept the lollipop woman's assistance or wait for my mum to appear at the living room window and signal that it was safe to cross.

I knew if I walked up to the end of the street, the lollipop woman, who sported a visibility coat, peaked cap and large intimidating looking stick, would acknowledge me with a "Hey there". This would make me feel extremely uncomfortable and under pressure to respond. For me, it was a no-brainer – the least anxiety-provoking option had to be option two, to wait for my mum to appear at the window. For the most part, this strategy worked well, and my mum usually managed to time it perfectly for my approach. However, on a couple of occasions, she was distracted by her busy schedule and lost track of time, leaving me standing on the opposite side of the road.

On one occasion, I waited for what felt like an hour. In reality, it was probably closer to 20 minutes. Most of the school children had disappeared and the road was free from traffic, apart from the odd car passing by. It would have been easy for me to cross the road by myself: maybe I wouldn't have been in trouble, since my mum had not fulfilled her part of the deal. However, rules are rules. There was no way I was going to disobey my mum. Even when the lollipop woman, now free of her duties, was edging closer towards me, I just stood there waiting anxiously for the inevitable.

As expected, the lollipop woman attempted to converse with me: "hey there, how are you?" My response was muted. My head was down and my eyes were firmly fixated on the ground as I waited in angst for her to step onto the road and signal that it was safe to cross. As soon as she did, I hurriedly ran across the road, and up the steps to my front door. I quickly opened the door and shut it with gratitude.

Fanny's Mum

During the holidays, I spent most of my time in the great outdoors. I often climbed over my back wall to play with Matthew, whose home backed onto ours. My best friend Stuart lived around the corner from me too, so our duo often became a trio. We would do all sorts of boisterous things like climbing trees, playing football, shooting each other with toy guns or attacking strangers with water pistols. We would sometimes also venture into unauthorised territory – usually involving overcoming obstacles such as high walls and overgrown bushes full of nettles. On rainy days, we would play *Mario* or *Duck Hunt* on the Nintendo. I enjoyed playing with boys and did not feel the need to have female friends. I had no desire to engage in "gender appropriate activities" such as playing with *Barbie* or talking about hair and make-up, like most other girls of my age. This is not to say I didn't like girls or never wanted to play with them; however, the girls I did choose to play with were by no means "girly girls".

I idolised Stuart – he was not just a friend, but also a mentor who I looked up to and wanted to be like. I would often copy him and I frequently asked my mother to buy me something purely because he had it. It wasn't just Stuart I liked to copy – I remember on one occasion I pleaded with my mum to buy me *Nike* trainers, in an attempt to be more like a boy a couple of years older than me. This went on for weeks until my mum eventually succumbed to my powers of persuasion.

I remember sitting in class one day, in my usual diligent manner, when a boy shouted out, "Fanny's mum at the door" (Fanny was my nickname at school). *Oh God*, I thought, hiding my head in my jumper. As I looked up, I noticed her eyes peering through the glass panel at the bottom of the classroom door. She actually had to lie down to be able to see into the classroom! *Ground, please swallow me up.* The teacher responded to the commotion in the class and went out to see what all the fuss was about. She quickly reappeared and asked me to leave the classroom. At this point, I was both concerned and apprehensive. *What could my mum possibly have to say that is so important she feels the need to take me out of class? Had someone close to me been injured or even worse, killed in a road accident?* My fears were quickly diminished as she pulled out a bag with the *Nike* trainers I had so desperately wanted. I was embarrassed but also secretly pleased. The rest of the class were in stitches.

This was neither the first, nor the last time my mum turned up at my school unannounced. When I was in primary, my mum appeared on numerous occasions at the school dinner hut, peering through the window, searching for her children to embarrass them for her own entertainment. Once she spotted us, she would press her face up against the window, making it look distorted for effect.

The kids in our school adored her – they thought she was great fun and often wanted to come to our house to play, or more accurately, to be entertained by my mother. My friends had high expectations and I was determined to make their experience a good one. I would warn my mum in advance to put on a good show and she always surpassed my expectations. She usually achieved this by behaving in the following way: in preparation for my friend coming over, she would wait at the hall window, ready to flash her boobs.

Upon arrival, she would lift and lower her top, multiple times and in quick succession to entertain a bemused teenage girl. I remember one friend in particular, who would attempt to avert her eyes from the window, while secretly enjoying the show. I know this because I watched her from the bedroom window as she was approaching. Her slight smirk soon turned into laughter that she could no longer contain.

When she was barely in the front door, my friend would be greeted with "It's so nice to meet you. I have heard all about you and I am sorry I am so fat". "Er…that's ok and it's nice to meet you too", my friend would reply in between bursts of laughter. Then the embarrassing questions would follow. "Have you started your periods yet?" or "Have you ever had sex with your boyfriend?" followed by "Oh, good for you, don't let him think you are easy".

My friends, for the most part, enjoyed the banter and encouraged her to perform. I think they appreciated her openness and willingness to discuss any topic. In fact, my closest friends did on occasion approach her to discuss personal matters that would have been too awkward to talk about with their own family. My mum has a magical way of making people feel welcome and immediately comfortable in her presence, despite the awkward questions and somewhat odd behaviour. I can honestly say there has never been a dull moment in the Baird household, thanks to my mother and her unusual ways.

A Dying Child

For most of my childhood, my anxiety manifested itself through recurring thoughts of death and physical illness. I was obsessed with every spot, lump or mark on my body, convinced that it was some form of cancer that would, in the not-so-distant future (usually within a year at most), inevitably end my life. I can honestly say that these unhealthy and persistent thoughts had a negative impact on every one of my childhood experiences.

I can vividly recall a few instances that show the negative impact these thoughts had on my life. I was 14 years old and in fourth year at school, working towards my Standard Grades. I was sitting in registration when there was an announcement that the entire school had to meet in the assembly hall. We were informed that a boy in my year had contracted tuberculosis and was in hospital receiving treatment. Even the mere mention of physical illness was enough to make my heart race. As our headmistress reeled off a list of symptoms, I felt myself becoming more and more agitated. Then the big words came… LIFE THREATENING and CONTAGIOUS!

Well, that was me for the rest of the day… I was in a world of my own, completely consumed by repetitive thoughts of tuberculosis (the only learning I did that day) and desperately trying to determine the probability of contracting this life-threatening airborne disease. *Okay, so what did the head mistress say again*? Tuberculosis is caused by bacteria that spread from person to person. This can happen when someone with the untreated, active form of tuberculosis, coughs, speaks, sneezes or laughs. Although it is contagious, it is hard to catch.

Actually, did she say that last bit about it being hard to catch? No, I don't think so. Okay, so statistically speaking, what are the chances of me having this LIFE-THREATENING disease? I am not friends with the boy, nor am I in any of his classes. Okay, great. Now when did I last see him? I walked past him in the corridor last week. How close was I to him? Did he brush past me? Was there actual contact? Was he speaking at the time? I can't remember! This is harder than I thought. We have been in close proximity many times – I am sure of it! His group usually congregate at the entrance to the school, approximately ten metres from where our group stand.

In this way, I concluded that there would have been many opportunities for me catch the disease.

Okay, so now we have a tick against the contagious aspect, now let's look at the symptoms. A cough – I have had a persistent cough for a few weeks now; coughing up blood – I have noticed red specks in my phlegm; unintentional weight loss – I am very thin, despite eating like a horse. Have I lost weight recently? Fatigue – I have been falling asleep on the bus going home from school recently. This must mean I am suffering from fatigue. Conclusion – I have tuberculosis and I am going to die!

I can still remember the journey home on the bus that day. The bus was crowded with schoolchildren, most of whom were standing, allowing the elderly and mothers with children to occupy the seats. On this occasion, I was fortunate enough to get a seat, not that it really mattered as I could have been anywhere at that moment in time. I was in a state of shock, having just found out my terrible fate. The sun was blinding, forcing me to shut my eyes. I struggled to stay awake as I surrendered to the "fatigue".

My parents were on holiday and my nana was looking after my siblings and me for a week. When I returned home from school, I went to the garden where my nana was hanging out the washing. I wanted to tell her. I wanted her to comfort me so badly. But I was afraid. I was scared of upsetting her and I did not want my parents to find out the terrible truth while they were on holiday enjoying themselves. So, I decided instead, to suffer in silence, just as I had always done.

"Having an early night nana. I am not feeling well," I said, and off I went to my bedroom, making sure I did not bump into my brother or sister on the stairs to avoid having to engage in conversation.

I have always found it easier to fall asleep when I am in the depths of depression. I think this is because sleep provides escape: it is the only time I am free from my thoughts. I did not, could not eat for two whole days following my self-diagnosis. It was a combination of not feeling hungry and… well, what was the point in eating when I was going to die soon anyway? These thoughts stayed with me for a couple of days until I was ready to divulge the information to my nana. "Nana, I have tuberculosis and I am going to die". I was taken aback by her response; "It's all in your head Francesca. You do not have TB". "Yes but I have the symptoms… and a boy in my school has it… and how can you be certain that it's not TB?"

It took a while, but eventually she managed to reassure me, and my symptoms miraculously diminished a short time later. After three or four days of what I can only describe as the feelings someone encounters during the initial stages of grief (shock, anger, despair), I began to consider the possibility that perhaps, at least at this point in my life, I did not have tuberculosis.

Unfortunately (and ironically), my anxieties about dying remained persistent. Although, the tuberculosis episode is perhaps the most extreme example, I must have driven my parents crazy as I sought reassurance on a regular basis. Typical ailments included various types of cancer, a brain tumour and anorexia (despite eating a lot and deliberately trying to put on weight). When I was 12, I identified a small fatty lump on the inside of my mouth. I obsessively caressed it with my tongue for weeks on end, trying to determine if it was getting bigger or changing shape. A dentist's appointment was looming, and I was terrified of being diagnosed with mouth cancer.

Unknown to me, my mum had phoned my dentist before my appointment and asked him to locate the lump and offer me re-assurance. He duly informed me that it was just a fatty lump and nothing sinister. He was hugely experienced, and he told me he had seen patients with mouth cancer and could discriminate between my lump and a more sinister mass. I had no reason to doubt his judgement. Almost reluctantly, I accepted his diagnosis and tempo-rarily freed my mind from thoughts of illness. I still have the lump to this day – although it does not bother me anymore.

Another common source of anxiety stemmed from thoughts of having a brain tumour. Despite never having had a migraine, I have, from time to time, had what I can only describe as a tender scalp and feelings of light-headedness. During such times, I would obsessively feel my head for lumps and bumps, as did my parents (I gave them little choice). Of course, my parents knew that it was most likely to be a symptom of the common cold or an infection, but they duly played along. Their reassurance helped to suppress my anxieties for a brief period before they resurfaced with a vengeance. I did accept that the risk of suffering from a tumour was small, but as long as it remained a possibility, I felt I had every reason to worry.

I have always been what might be described as petite. During my teens I must have weighed approximately five and a half stone. I am not sure if I was underweight, but I was significantly lighter than every one of my female peers – to the point where a number of my friends commented on my weight, questioning if I was anorexic. As I am someone who worries excessively about their weight, this was not well received.

I was already paranoid about my weight and often wore baggy clothes to try and hide the fact I was skinny. In hindsight, this probably wasn't the best idea: the clothes just hung on me, making me look even thinner. Ironically, I have always had a healthy appetite. I absolutely adore food and eat more that anyone I know. People are often shocked by the amount of food on my plate and even more surprised by the speed at which it disappears. My close friend Sara, who is very conscious of my relationship with food, would cleverly use this knowledge as a negotiation tactic to entice me over to her house and, in turn, make me more sociable. "Do you want to come and stay the night at my house?" While I was thinking of a plausible excuse, she would quickly follow this question with, "We can order a Chinese". Invariably, I was there in 20 minutes.

I spent a lot of time monitoring my weight and examining my body contours in the mirror. Observing a side view provoked the greatest level of anxiety. I looked seriously ill, like a dying person does when their body stops accepting food and rapidly deteriorates. *How can someone who eats as much as I do be so skinny and incapable of putting on weight?* Possible explanations such as genetics or high metabolism fleetingly crossed my mind but were quickly dismissed as they weren't interesting enough. There could only be one explanation… a huge worm in my intestines was eating my food. I also thought this would explain the sudden weight loss – two whole pounds in just under a week! I had hit the nail on the head: it was a Eureka moment! It was as if, somehow, I would feel better for identifying the cause of my perceived illness, which was unlikely, as the diagnosis was inevitably terminal.

Hospitals and doctors were no go areas for me. Fortunately, I had no reason to visit a hospital as a child. I was however, forced to visit the doctor on a couple of occasions: once for a rash and once for a persistent sickness. Like many challenging situations in life, the thought of going to the doctors was significantly worse than the experience itself.

I did not like the idea of being in close proximity to the person examining me – it felt both intimate and intrusive. In that moment, my body was vulnerable. I was vulnerable. Control over my body was temporarily transferred to the doctor, who would determine my fate. As usual, my brain went into overdrive and the questions emerged:

What if she decides the rash is meningitis and rushes me to hospital? What if she notices that I am underweight and sends me for further tests? I was also convinced that they would find the worm eating away at my intestines. *What if she monitors my heart rate and finds an anomaly that is totally unrelated to anything else, but equally as dangerous to my health?* I am sure there were more "what ifs", but you get the drift. I felt extremely uncomfortable as the doctor asked me to pull up my top to inspect the rash. I think I would have passed out if she asked me to pull down my trousers. Diagnosis: an infection that required antibiotics.

I am extremely sensitive to my environment and struggle to separate my experiences from the location in which they are experienced. I think, in some ways, this is quite common. For example, imagine someone is walking their dog when, just as they approach the entrance to the forest path, they are savagely attacked. What are the chances of that person gladly returning to the site of the attack? My guess is that they wouldn't, since the specific location is likely to trigger physiological responses and negative emotions.

The problem for me was that my health anxieties were so frequent and severe – to the point where I honestly believed that I was going to imminently die – that I somehow managed to create deeply negative associations in a wide variety of locations, making it much harder to escape my anxieties.

Although my health anxieties have diminished over the years, the feelings triggered by such "areas" are still with me. My main anxiety zone includes anywhere within a four-mile radius of my old house. This entire area is an activation point for my anxiety and is the main reason why I avoid places that remind me of my childhood.

I am particularly sensitive to one street, Rosemount Viaduct, which runs perpendicular to the road where the secondary school I attended is. When I say sensitive, what I mean is, I would rather be dead than live on that street. This is not an exaggeration.

I associate what I call my "danger zone" with fear, confusion, loss of identity and loss of control. I cannot even drive along this street without having an emotional reaction: if I did, I would be unable to shake off the negative feelings for most of the day. It seems like the location simultaneously triggers negative thoughts and physiological symptoms. There is not one single item that sets off my anxiety. It is the whole street and everything it represents – my childhood – that triggers my emotions. I am sure that, if I closed my eyes as I entered the viaduct and did not open them again until I was on a different street, I would still feel the same emotions. Mental images would replace actual images, and they would provoke the same response.

The physiological symptoms of this anxiety include a racing heart rate, an increase in temperature and a rigid body. This is accompanied by thought processes that go a little like this…

This street reminds me of my childhood. It is near my old school and the area where I grew up… I feel extremely uncomfortable. Imagine I had to live here, that would be like torture… could I ever live here? No, absolutely not…Who am I? I have temporarily lost my identity… I need to try and control this situation and make things right in my head… but I can't. Everything I know and feel is lost in this present moment… this street reminds me of my childhood.

These obsessive, repetitive thoughts may dissipate slightly as I leave the location behind. However, I often find that it takes a while for me to adjust and make sense of things after what I can only describe as a traumatic experience. If I go straight home, the feeling stays with me, and it even affects the way I feel about familiar places, primarily my home. It feels different. I feel different. I feel like I am an intruder in my own home. Familiar surroundings that usually induce happy feelings are temporarily tarnished and unable to comfort me like they usually do. It is a confusing, scary experience for someone whose identity is deeply intertwined with their environment.

Gradually, my surroundings do begin to feel familiar again. By the following morning, my sense of self has returned, and I am almost back to being me again, although still fragile and exhausted.

In order to avoid "trigger zones", I often take detours, adding miles to my journey home. I find that by taking a familiar route home, feelings of safety, control and contentment supersede the negative feelings. Having approached my home from the 'correct' direction, my brain is recalibrated, and things feel right again.

Comfort Zone

As I enter the front door to my flat, the familiar sound of my dog barking reassures me. I go to the kitchen and pour myself a *Nespresso*. The resulting smell of caramel coffee comforts my senses. I should tidy but I am exhausted. I walk through to the living room and recline in my usual spot on the sofa. I stare out of the glass balcony doors at the stunning view of hills beyond the golf course. Today, the view is perceived positively: it is both a familiar and comforting scene. I realise that my environment is as it should be and I feel protected from everything outside my own bubble. My mum calls but I ignore the phone since I don't have the energy to speak. It has been a challenging day (it always is) and I need time, in isolation, to recharge my batteries. I feel a sudden desire to eat. I am hungry and irritable, so I order an Indian takeaway. I switch the TV on and search for a good drama before settling on a series about a psychotherapist and his weekly sessions with patients called *In Treatment*. When my food arrives, I pause the TV so I can fully immerse myself in the process of eating. I don't always know how I am feeling but at this moment in time, I know that I am truly happy.

School Days

Primary school was a relatively easy experience for me. I had friends, both boys and girls, who I would play with at lunchtime and occasionally meet at the weekend. I have always been very athletic. In fact, I was probably one of the best in my class at every sport I turned to, which put me in good stead for making friends. This is unlike the experience of many autistic people, for whom poor motor coordination and lack of spatial awareness can make it difficult for them to perform well in sporting activities, compared to their neurotypical peers. This in turn can contribute to difficulties in making friends and the individual feeling isolated. I guess I was fortunate in this respect – everyone wanted to be on Fanny's team.

Lunchtime at school consisted of a very rushed, short eating session, followed by 50 minutes of continuous play. Football, man hunt and the tennis ball game were among my favourites. I was a talented footballer, by far the best in my class. I could even run circles round the boys, which was unusual as football was a predominantly male sport at that time. I was also fantastic as "keepie uppies" and was not afraid to demonstrate my skills in public.

For those of you who are not familiar with man hunt, it is a game with two teams: the hiders and the seekers. It is basically a variation of hide and seek but for the older, cool kids. Unsurprisingly, I was always the last one found. This was because I was incredibly fast and could outrun the catchers, allowing me to dart from one hide out to the next. The tennis ball game involves two teams: each team has alternative shots at throwing the ball to the opposing side of the court. The opposition has to try and catch the ball to prevent the throwing team from obtaining points. The further the throw, the more points awarded. The team with the most points wins. I had a pretty mean right hand throw, one of the best in fact. I also caught many of the opposition's throws, hugely contributing to our team's win.

I used sport as my gateway into the social world, as it was an opportunity to feel part of a group without having to engage in conversation. As long as I was participating in group sports, I was safe with the knowledge that I had friends, who I shared common interests with. Little did I know that, by the time I reached secondary school, social expectations would have moved on to something less active in nature and more conversation-based: and when it came to the girls, the conversations would usually be about boys. Some of the worst years in my life, in terms of increased anxiety and feelings of social isolation, were yet to come.

Secondary school – what can I say? I despised every single moment of it. I felt uncomfortable as soon as I tried on my school uniform – a shirt, school blazer and… wait for it… a SKIRT! I had never worn a skirt in my life and I sure as hell didn't want to wear one then. I had only ever been comfortable in long trousers. Skirts were way too feminine and, in my eyes, completely pointless. To wear a skirt, you also had to wear tights! What was the point in wearing two layers instead of one? It's not even like they are comfortable. Of course, there would have been the option of wearing a skirt without tights, but then my legs would have been cold and exposed. Can you believe that some girls wear skirts without tights, all year round (super short ones, too, leaving not very much to the imagination)? I had no choice but to opt for the skirt and tights. You know the saying, feel good, look good, do good? Well, I certainly didn't feel good in my school uniform – pretty darn shit actually – so what were the chances of me doing good? Nada! Funny how a school uniform is supposed to represent unity and make people the same. Yet I could not have felt any more alone. Why were other girls so accepting of the school uniform? Probably because they felt comfortable in a skirt and were happy to promote their femininity. I was different. But I was under pressure to conform.

I was separated from my friends at secondary school as we were all in different classes. This left me with no option but to try and develop new friendships, and quickly. I knew what I had to do to fit in and made every effort to be "one of the girls". I developed a friendship group with five other girls, one of whom I am still friends with. Socialising with boys was no longer an option. Oh, well actually, that is not strictly true. I was allowed to talk to boys, flirt with them and perhaps even date some. However, society tells us that girls and boys are different – not just genetically but in terms of their interests, personalities and behavioural traits. There are expectations about female etiquette and so I did what I had to do to conform (masking my differences). At break and lunch, we would often congregate by the radiator, just outside the head teacher's door. As school is in the centre of town, we had many options for lunch. It was usually the sandwich shop, *Heavenly Pizza* (my favourite), the newsagents (by far my least favourite), the Chinese noodle shop or *McDonalds*. On the odd occasion, we went to *Baskin Robbins* for an ice cream lunch – missing out on a proper lunch, which never left me feeling satisfied. As I was not in a position to dictate where we went for lunch each day (it was usually decided by a group consensus), some days were good, and some days were bad. That was just the way it was and I had to get on with it the best I could. Sadly, playing football was no longer an option for me unless, of course, I wanted to play football with the wall and be perceived as a loner.

In the classroom, I spent most of time in my own head, consumed by my thoughts and unable to digest the teacher's words. I felt out of my depth, crippled with social anxiety and unable to focus on anything external to my own mind. I felt out of place, inadequate and inferior to my young adult peers.

I was a lost little girl, desperately trying to find her way in life. I didn't know anything about anything, and I was sure everyone else was aware of my stupidity. If the teacher asked me a question, I was not prepared to embarrass myself by pretending I knew the answer. Even if I had an inkling of the answer, I was unlikely to risk being wrong. Consequently, "I don't know" was my typical response.

I looked on as the rest of the class raised their hands, ready to answer what I can only assume was a simple question. My only saving grace was my ability to study in the comfort of my home. Not only could I retain information for just as long as I needed to answer exam questions, but I could also reiterate what I had learned under exam conditions, and successfully. Through this method of learning, I was fortunate enough to pass all my exams, both at Standard Grade and at Higher level.

The only subject I particularly enjoyed in school was maths – a subject that has an answer that is not down to interpretation. I would quite happily spend time trying to solve an equation and felt a great sense of satisfaction when I discovered the answer. I could easily get absorbed in maths, not giving up until the question was answered and understood. By contrast, English was by far my worst subject at school. The reasons for this are: my language is restrictive, I have no imagination and poetry is something I have never understood.

Writing essays was, and always has been a struggle for me. My thoughts are a jumbled mess, and I think this comes across in my writing style. I could cope with the basics but as soon I was asked to use my imagination or use descriptive language, I found I was out of my depth. Questions that required analysis and interpretation of text were completely beyond my remit. As such, my essays were often short and to the point, lacking any real substance. Despite my failings, I managed to scrape through Higher English – I still don't know how, but I won't complain.

I somehow managed to avoid being bullied during my first four years of secondary school, probably due to strength in numbers; I had at least one of my five friends in every class, shielding me from any bullying. However, things changed when I entered the fifth year and made the brave decision to choose subjects based on my strengths rather than because my friends were taking them. This inevitably made me vulnerable. When I was not with my friends, I was shy and introverted. Physically a late developer, I was still small, and right through Secondary School, this made me an easy target for bullying. On the first day of Higher Art, I entered the classroom only to find that we had all been assigned seats. I was indifferent to this as I did not know anyone anyway. Unfortunately, I was assigned a seat next to a boy who quickly detected my vulnerabilities and made it his mission to assert his authority over me. It started with commands, "Go and get me the paint". Initially I tried to ignore him. However, he became more assertive and quite aggressive in his tone, "GO AND GET ME THE PAINT". This was usually enough to make me comply.

I was not strong enough to defend myself and I had no one there to protect me. I didn't want to tell the teacher either, as I did not want to be perceived as a "snitch" and I was worried that it would make the situation worse. "That is the wrong colour of paint, go and get me a different colour". I soon realised that it was easier to give in to his demands than confront him, so I did everything he asked of me. I sat at a table of four with two other girls and not one of them defended me. In hindsight, I think he picked on me to impress a girl that was sitting opposite me, as they started dating shortly after. I wouldn't have thought that bullying was an attractive trait, but each to their own I guess.

After a few weeks of the same silly comments and demands, out popped something new, a song this time: "I'm sitting beside a little dwarf doo doo... I'm sitting beside a little dwarf". If I had been smart, I would have hit back with some witty remark to put this immature little boy back in his box. However, I didn't have the words. Instead, I silently endured his silly demands, hurtful comments and fantastically original songs for the best part of a year, and it didn't end there either.

One lunchtime, he unexpectedly caught me, grabbed me, and shoved me into a cage. Yes, a cage! Actually, I think it was probably a bike shed or something of that sort, but to me it was a cage: the door was made of steel bars with a big lock on the front. He shoved me in and quickly shut the door before I had the chance to retaliate. As if that wasn't enough, he began to spit through the bars, deliberately trying to cover me in his saliva. Fortunately, the cage was deep and I managed to move far enough back to avoid the saliva barrage. I was in shock and complete disbelief. *What could I possibly have done to this boy to deserve such treatment? Is this a punishment of some sort?* I wanted to cry but how could I? People would think I was being pathetic and weak, and I didn't want to embarrass myself any more than I had to. Laughing and trying to brush it off wasn't an option either, since it was not really a laughing matter.

A crowd started to gather to see what the commotion was all about. My friends desperately tried to reason with him but he was not willing to let his target go. Eventually, some prefects from the year above intervened and freed me from my prison.

"How was your day at school, love?"

"Fine", I said as I threw my bags on the floor and went straight up to my bedroom to release my emotions in solitude. I didn't want my parents to know – partly because I didn't want them to worry, but mostly because I wanted to shut myself off from the rest of the world and pretend it had never happened. I think this was pretty much the extent of the bullying during my time at secondary school.

Oh now wait… hold on… actually, there was that time a boy threatened to stab me with a compass in Spanish class… and the time a boy pushed me to the ground and kicked me in the chest over and over – all because I accidentally hit him with a football. But other than that, I led a relative "bullying free" childhood.

Oddly, other girls have never picked on me. Why, I do not know. Perhaps females feel intimidated or threatened by me? This is unlikely, given my petite frame and desire to avoid confrontation. The more likely explanation is my specific ability to mask my differences and blend in with the crowd. I may have managed to escape female bullying, but I was unhappy, and I felt incredibly isolated.

Under pressure to conform to societal pressure and expectations of how a girl should appear physically and behave socially, I was exhausted and confused. Without the tools to express my emotions, I concluded that there was no point discussing my feelings with family or friends. They wouldn't understand. I didn't understand. I had no option but to internalise my emotions as I had always done. But I didn't realise that, by suppressing my emotions, I was doing myself more harm than good. It was only a matter of time before the accumulation of deeply embedded negative emotions would resurface. I was not prepared for the whirlwind of emotions I would eventually encounter.

Entering The World Of Work

My first job was short lived. I was 15 years old and desperate to establish some independence and, in turn, earn some money. My mum helped me get a job in a local chip shop and, as my sister worked there already, I pretty much had it in the bag. Just as well really since the interview was a disaster! Well, perhaps this is a little harsh, but it did demonstrate my naivety and inexperience. When asked about my hobbies, I responded with "er… I enjoy cleaning dishes". I knew this was a big part of the job role and thus thought this was the most appropriate answer: a mistake I have since learned from.

The job was much harder than anticipated, too. I struggled to cope with the fast-paced nature of it and the need to multitask – holding a conversation, while writing down an order and collecting plates all at the same time was for me an almost impossible task. It was a busy place and the whole experience was overwhelming for me. To make matters worse, one of the managers approached me during my second shift and said, with what I thought was an inappropriate tone, "THE CUPS ARE SUPPOSED TO BE CLEAN". He must have thought I was useless and could not do the job. There was no way I could face him again. "Screw this", I thought. "I am out of here". Only I was too embarrassed to call, so instead, and without an explanation, I did not turn up to my next shift.

This would become a recurring behavioural pattern in relation to work in later years, though I didn't know that at the time. I don't think my sister was very impressed either as she had to make up some excuse about me not being well and unable to resume my role as the crap cup cleaner – which was kind of ironic given I'd claimed it was my hobby.

My second job was much more of a success. My mum, once again, worked her magic to land me a role as a sales assistant in *The Natural World*: an awesome little store that sold random rocks, cool experimental science kits, refractor and reflector telescopes and a host of other space and science-related toys. It was a fun job, one in which my role was to serve customers and replenish stock: all manageable tasks, even for me. I only worked weekends as I was still in my sixth year at school and working towards my Highers, but it was enough to give me a feel of what it was like to be part of the working world.

It was a small team of five, creating an intimate environment, reminiscent of my own little family. My colleagues were all female, much older than me and, for some unknown reason, they thought I was hilarious. Half the time, I wasn't sure if they were laughing at me or with me but I didn't really care. They seemed to like the newly unearthed version of me and they were more than willing to take me under their wing, making me feel both safe and protected from the outside world.

For the first time in my life, I felt that I had a purpose, and that I truly belonged. When I was at work, I was in my comfort zone and free from the negative thoughts that had caused so much internal pain. The version of me I portrayed (or at least my guess as to how others perceived me) in the work environment was someone quiet, diligent, focused, witty and with the potential to achieve great things in life: in other words, it was the person I wanted to be.

When engaged in group conversation with my colleagues, I would observe and listen intently, only adding the odd comment that was usually either brutally honest or sarcastic. I think this made me appear intelligent, when, in fact, I didn't have anything to say about any subject matter I didn't already know about. I guess you could say that I was using humour as a front, to hide my insecurities, lack of knowledge and inability to express myself. Regardless, it was a version of me that I liked, and which enabled me to feel comfortable in my own skin.

I remember our first staff night out: a Christmas do at an Italian restaurant located within a five-minute walk from my work. There were eight of us in total (five staff and three partners). I had just turned 16, so I was an adult by definition, and was excited to participate in a social get together with my newfound friends and mentors. As the night was in full flow, I decided to let my hair down and neck a few vodkas, just enough to make a newbie drinker tipsy. With increased confidence, I had much more to say: I can recall the group talking about me and laughing on numerous occasions, making me the centre of attention. Frustratingly, I cannot recall what I did or said that was so funny, but I can imagine how I would have come across – reserved and quiet to begin with, simply taking it all in. Then, as the evening progressed and my confidence grew, I would have thrown in a few comments or asked a direct question, usually something inappropriate but seemingly well received in any case.

If my memory serves me well, at one point I said something along the lines of "Your husband it much younger and more attractive that I imagined". Everyone laughed at such a random, unexpected statement, leading to more in-depth conversations about age and relationships. I knew what I was doing of course, acting as an instigator to get people talking during the quiet, uneventful moments. Having determined the subject matter, I was then able to sit back and listen to the conversation flow without any further input. For the most part, this strategy seemed to work well: allowing me to engage in a conversation while appearing to spend the rest of my time processing and contemplating the meaning through deeper levels of conversation.

In reality I had nothing to say, but it was important for me to appear to be an intelligent, thoughtful young woman. Interestingly,

I was so focused on making it an enjoyable night out for everyone involved, that I had a complete disregard for my surroundings and was thus free from anxious thoughts that might otherwise have been triggered by my environment.

My behaviour at work was similar. I did not mind interacting with customers because of the precise nature of the conversation. I found selling a product much easier than having neutral conversations that had no real purpose or intent. It was like I had a script and I had learned how to perform, in order to fulfil my role successfully as a sales assistant.

Of course, my ability and attitude to work did not go unnoticed, as I was often praised for my dedication and hard work. It is therefore only natural that I wanted to cling on to this particular part of my life (the work, the people, and the environment) and the feelings it provoked for as long as I could.

A Fantasy World

My time working at *The Natural World* signified a new stage in my life. Not only had I developed a sense of self, but I had also developed an intense attraction to a security guard who worked in the shopping centre. Looking back, he was not attractive and a little overweight… well, perhaps a lot overweight. But he had something: an intense, smouldering look. I had only ever seen him walking around the centre but there was something that drew me to him: that elusive thing that attracts you to someone, even though you do not know, consciously, what that thing is.

I could feel his eyes burning right through me as I walked past him on my way to and from work and I was certain that he had a crush on me, which in turn made me feel great about myself. His good-looking brother from another mother worked in the centre too, but I had no interest in him. He was far too attractive and had a string of girls after him. Steve, my chosen brother, looked significantly older than me and he didn't have the good looks, but perhaps I saw him as an attainable goal.

At 16 years old, I was becoming increasingly aware of my sexuality and the power of the feminine form. I was still petite: a late developer, I had only just started my periods and my boobs were still growing. I would describe myself, at that time in my life, as incredibly young looking with an air of innocence. My fantasy about this older man was fresh and exciting. I was a virgin, and it was the first time I had thought about someone sexually, or at least the first time that the notion of sex had generated feelings of pure elation.

I frequently conjured up an image of what sex with Steve would be like, and this kept the fantasy alive. I was continually thinking about his perception of me, and I became much more interested in my physical appearance. Since my fantasy was built purely on imagination, and fuelled by visual stimulation, it was important for me to nail my dress code so that he would see me in a specific way.

On Friday evenings, I spent a lot of time preparing my outfit for work, ensuring I had a belt to match every outfit, or more likely, an outfit to match my belt – with an obsession for belts, I had a collection of 50 or more, which was perhaps a bit excessive. On a casual day, I would wear khaki combat trousers, a slip belt, a pair of *Converse* trainers and a tight long-sleeved t-shirt or jumper. A dressier outfit would consist of black wide-legged trousers, small heels, a big-buckled belt and a tight black top. Suddenly, for the first time in my life, I found myself dressing to impress, which was a novel, exciting experience. I had different looks depending on my mood and whether I wanted to look cute, or older and mature. However, I never wore anything revealing as I didn't feel comfortable showing flesh and did not want to deviate completely from my tomboy persona. Having chosen my outfit, I would try it on, put on some music (usually Michelle Branch or Avril Lavigne) and look at myself in the mirror, trying to imagine how I would appear to the opposite sex: more specifically, how I would appear to Steve. I had created an image of the kind of woman Steve would like and it was important for me to perfect this look: someone naïve and innocent, who he could teach about sex and relationships. I was still in my sixth year at school, and as I already had the grades to get into university, I wished that I could somehow pass this information on to him. As I've said, it was important to me to appear to be intelligent. I don't know why this was so important to me. Maybe it was because, on some level, I was aware of my deficits: inflexible, repetitive thinking, which prevented me from seeing the bigger picture or thinking "outside the box". The unique way my brain processed information made it difficult for me to seek new opportunities and prevented me from opening my mind to a world outside my own head.

For almost six months, I failed to overtly acknowledge Steve. I had of course spotted him from afar – using my in-built Steve detection system – allowing me to spot him wherever he was in the centre. This included the use of mirror reflections and his bright orange shirt (the security uniform) to assist with the identification process. A typical Steve experience, involved walking past each other, heading in opposite directions and often metres apart. I would keep my eyes focused firmly in front to avoid any kind of eye contact, but I could sense him looking at me, which was enough to keep me satisfied until the next time. It was even better if I had a friend who I could be seen talking to or laughing with as he passed, introducing a slightly different dynamic to the scene. As school was only 15 minutes from the centre, I would use my free periods to go into town for a thrilling "walk by Steve" experience. My friends were more than happy to spend their free time shopping, so it was a win-win situation all round. After each social encounter, I would analyse every little detail – had he seen me? From what angle had he seen me? Had I been laughing or engaged in conversation? Had he liked my new belt? Had he even spotted it?

I hoped it was no coincidence that he was standing in the exact spot overlooking the ground floor since this is where he would have the best view of me walking past. Later that day, at home, I would play Michelle Branch's "Everywhere" on repeat while looking at myself in the mirror (for up to a couple of hours at a time), trying to see myself from his perspective. I was doing this to generate excitement and fuel my fantasy. Suddenly, I was no longer thinking about illness and death: I had found a new interest to consume my thoughts. It seemed a "healthier" obsession, which was more aligned with my friends' love interests. It could only be a good thing, right?

Our first actual conversation occurred when I was standing behind the desk, counting the day's takings. I looked up and... holy crap, there he was right in front of me. He was with a little boy (his nephew apparently), which I could only assume was to cover the real reason he was in my shop: to see me. I was flustered and flabbergasted but determined to keep my cool. "Hi, how is it going? I am looking for something for my nephew. Any ideas?" I went for options that were reasonably priced and popular with the kids, showing him a pack of touch bubbles and an erupting volcano. He quickly made his decision and opted for the touch bubbles. To be honest, I think he would have taken anything just to speak to me. I could hardly hide the physical effect he was on having on me: I was shaking as I scanned the item and took his money; my heart was racing and I could hardly breathe. I am sure he must have noticed the nervousness I was trying to so hard to hide.

I had been obsessing over this man for six months and to be finally speaking to him was enthralling and completely unexpected. After he left, I had to wait a good few minutes to come down from cloud nine and for my heart rate to return to normal. Unsurprisingly, I spent the remainder of my shift in my head, replaying the conversation over and over, trying to decipher what every word had meant and what his intentions had been. I had noticed a couple of his front teeth were missing when he smiled at me but that didn't matter – in fact, it made him more appealing since I had quite nice teeth and would therefore be more appealing to him, I thought. *Holy crap, he smiled!* Actual communication is not something I had seriously considered when I had developed my interest in Steve. This added a whole new dynamic to the situation and gave me plenty to think about when I got home that evening. My obsession had reached a new level of intensity and I was excited to see how things would develop.

On my next shift, my colleague dropped something significant into the conversation – we had all been invited to a party at Steve's flat the following Saturday. She said it so casually, like it was no big deal; but to me it was an unbelievable development. To say that my excitement levels went through the roof is a complete understatement. I was ecstatic.

I began to plan the next steps, which included the purchase of a new outfit, and trying to decide which belt would be the centrepiece of my attire. My mum helped me choose an outfit the night before the big event and she even supplied lipstick and mascara to complement the outfit. At the end of our shift, my colleagues helped me get ready by straightening my hair and applying some blusher to brighten my sallow cheeks. I wore a red V-neck T-shirt, the bright red lipstick courtesy of my mother, skinny jeans and a pair of stilettos, heel size no bigger than 1.5 inches (any bigger and people would think I was a prostitute, or so my mum told me anyway). This wasn't the only reason for the small heel – apparently it is better for balance and, as my mum has a real flare for fashion, I had no reason to doubt her.

There were not many of us at the party, possibly around ten in total. I started to wonder if it was only people from my shop who had been invited: this was an exciting notion. I sat down on the sofa, tugging on my colleague's top to bring her down beside me and to thus add a layer of protection against everyone else in the room. Steve, in gentlemanly fashion, was in the kitchen pouring the vodka and coke I had requested. While Steve was out of the way, my workmate asked one of the other security guards to divulge some facts about Steve on my behalf. I successfully learned that Steve owned his flat, was about 24 years of age and had been married, but thankfully had split after only six months of wedded bliss. He worked in a nightclub to supplement his income and he had no children.

To be honest, I could have been told he was a complete psychopath and it would not have made much difference. I would not have let anything ruin my infatuation that had become the focus of my thoughts and was giving me so much joy. I think we were at the party for a couple of hours at best. Steve and I had little communication. This is probably because I did my best to avoid him, spending most of my time engaged in conversation with one of the other security guards. It was all very civilised and unexciting apart from one... er... well... pretty darn significant development. As we stood up to exit the premises, Steve offered me his number! I had no hesitation accepting it, as I quickly extracted my phone from my back pocket and entered the name and number, hands trembling in the process. Mission accomplished!

After we left the party, the designated driver drove us into town; we were planning to make a night of it. I was 17 years old and had never been in a nightclub before. We had mentioned our intentions at the party and Steve, who worked at the nightclub, was adamant that I would never get past the door staff due to my young looks and the less significant fact that I was underage.

I was so nervous in the queue – I was tiny compared to everyone else... I was cursing my 0.5 inch heels and my mother for telling me what to wear. Gill, my friend and colleague, who had recently left the navy, had an idea. We would use my height as an advantage to get me past the bouncers. The plan was simple... there were four of us. Clare and Gill, who were both several years older than me and much taller, would build a wall of protection around me. Meanwhile Nicole, with her ridiculously good looks, would distract the bouncers so they could sneak me in, all the while maintaining my position in the middle of the pack. In true Francesca style, I made myself invisible and gained entrance to the club. I was on a roll that night, I tell you. Mission number two accomplished!

The club was of an overwhelming size, comprising three levels, two of which had their own dance floor, and there was a different genre of music playing on each floor. The first level was by far the biggest: it housed a random mix of people, both young and old, solo and in groups. On this floor, it was all about the atmosphere, having a laugh and enjoying a good boogie (not sure if people still use that word) to 90s pop music and the occasional modern song to keep the cool kids in town, irrespective of age or style. I was yet to discover this as at this point, as we headed straight for the cramped third floor, which had a bar and a small dance floor. I quickly discovered that this floor was where the bum pinching men hung out, on the prowl for attractive women who they could grind against while dancing to R&B. Here, on the third floor, the amount of interest a woman received in a night was calculated by the number of bum feels she received. Come to think of it, I don't think I got any bum feels on my first night in the club – not that it really mattered since I find this behaviour completely inappropriate... but still, it is always nice to know you are in demand. We spent the first few hours at the bar getting drunk on shots and vodka mixers. The latter half of the night entailed group dancing and a chicken kebab with chips as we stumbled along the street at 3am. This was followed by a sobering realisation of "oh shit I am working at 9am tomorrow".

As I lay in bed replaying the night's events. I couldn't believe I got his number. It was so surreal. I began asking myself the usual questions: *Did it really happen or am I tripping? Could all that mental effort have finally paid off?* Then it occurred to me; I had just got into the nightclub where the man I was interested in worked. Now I could see him, or rather he could see me, in a different setting. This was a new development and I was desperately trying to process this information and make sense of it. *Can I have your number? Can I have your number? Holy shit, did he ask for my number?* Every time I repeated this sentence, I pictured the exact moment he had said it, what he had been wearing, how he had been standing, his mannerisms and, perhaps most importantly, how I had responded. Had I come across as confident? Had he noticed me shaking? Had he looked at my belt as I walked away? I created multiple snapshot images of that moment in my mind. This, coupled with the sound of his voice, was the perfect combination for stimulating my brain into repetitive thoughts about Steve. With each thought, the reward system in my brain was activated, followed by positive physiological sensations, including an increased heart rate and the feeling of electricity running through my body. For the first time in my life, life was good (on the inside and outside).

First Date

It didn't take long for Steve to get in touch after the party. He approached me on my next shift, claiming that he wanted to know how the remainder of our night had gone. I took much pleasure in telling him that I had got into the club, as I thought this would impress him and perhaps add to my allure. There was a silence as I contemplated what to say next. As I have already explained, I wasn't a good conversationalist and had never been faced with this type of boy/girl scenario. Fortunately, my thoughts were interrupted as he followed up his question with another, more significant one: "Do you want to go on a date?" I replied with a simple "yes, sure" and he promised to contact me with the plans. I was happy with how the conversation had gone and did not want to ruin the progress we had made thus far by engaging in further conversation. He texted me later that day to suggest a mid-week date at an Italian restaurant near the shopping centre. I couldn't help but think to myself, *I am going on a date with a security guard, older than me and with his own car… suck on that bully boy at school.*

I think I put less effort into getting ready for the date than I had for the party at his house. In fact, I think I put more effort into my work outfits, in anticipation of seeing him in the centre. It would be wrong to say I wasn't excited about our date but as far as I was concerned, I had already achieved my goal: to be desired by Steve.

Our date was pleasant, with little conversation and plenty of food. To be honest, a date that involves food could never be terrible, regardless of the company. Besides, given the speed I eat at, there wasn't much time for conversation. Steve chivalrously paid for the meal (I did offer to contribute but he refused) and within an hour, we had both demolished our three-course meal and exited the building. The night was still young and we had plenty of time to take the party elsewhere. As Steve was driving, he suggested we go to his for a nightcap of sorts. I remember being impressed by his car, his driving, his manly persona... just everything, really. He was wearing a black jumper, blue jeans and work boots (very different and far more appealing than his work uniform). My memory of the jumper comes from a mental image I have of him in his car and not from the restaurant where we met: this is possibly because I could comfortably pick out these details while he was focused on the road ahead and was not looking directly at me.

I was nervous as we entered his flat: of course I was. It was just the two of us and despite my lack of experience when it came to dating, I had an inkling of how these things were supposed to go. I sat on the sofa, waiting patiently for him to make his move. He sat next to me briefly, before pulling us both down into a lying position so he could hug me from behind. I felt comfortable in that position – facing the opposite direction from him – since I was able to avoid eye contact. After an hour or so of hugging, I asked if he would take me home. "Before you go," he said. "Can I have a kiss?" He leaned over for a kiss and I responded dutifully. I did not feel the need to pull away so I can only assume that I enjoyed it. Then he moved things up a notch or two as he kissed my neck. This sent shivers right though me, a pleasant experience I had not encountered before.

Oh, I just remembered that I was wearing a plain tight white t-shirt with army trousers and a studded belt. It just popped into my mind as I pictured us on the sofa together, hugging and kissing. I was imagining how I had felt to him, specifically, the contours of my body. As I was thinking about it, I was much less concerned about how I felt about him – it is precisely this thought that triggered the image of the outfit. Anyway, the kiss was enough for one night and I was not prepared to take it any further. I was comfortable with how the night had progressed and I wanted to retain some control over the evening, including when it should end. A one-hour meal session followed by a couple of hours at his flat was more than enough for a first date, don't you think?

By allowing him to hug and kiss me, I felt that I had balanced things out and put us on an even keel. In other words, the cost of the meal and petrol was balanced out by the hug and a kiss. I perceived the evening as a win-win all round, and I was convinced that he was equally satisfied with how the night had unfolded: he certainly didn't protest when I asked for a lift home at around 9pm.

School felt different after that night. I was different. Suddenly, I was better equipped to cope with the mental stress of school and all it entails. I had bigger, better things going on in my life and school no longer held as much significance for me.

I was in my final few months of sixth year and had been accepted to study a Bachelor of Science in Psychology at *Aberdeen University*: ironic huh! I guess I had always been interested in the mind and how people think and behave. Or perhaps it is more likely that I wanted to understand my own brain and why I was different to everyone else. Either way, it was good to know that I would finally be escaping a life of misery for what could only be a happier, more fulfilling life. Additionally, I would have better control over my life. For example, I would have chosen the university to go to, I could choose the type of friends I would have and, crucially, I would have been able to wear whatever I wanted. Life suddenly had a new meaning and I was eager to enter the next stage of my life.

Okay, so let me reiterate where we are so far: I had created a fantasy about a man I did not know; I had somehow managed to gain his attention (despite not knowingly showing any overt interest in him); we had been on a date and kissed. All good so far, right? Well, no. I had a problem and I did not know how to deal with it. Everything was going well with Steve, so well in fact, that I questioned where it might end up going. In line with the natural progression of typical relationships, I assumed Steve would have expectations of how our relationship should develop. Again, I was consumed by repetitive thoughts and analysis: *Can I fulfil his expectations? Can I marry him? Can I even have sexual intercourse with him? If this becomes a reality, then surely it would inevitably lead to the development of an emotional and physical relationship. Am I ready for this and do I even want it?* As I processed these thoughts, the realisation that my fantasy was quickly becoming a reality began to sink in. Remarkably, this man had been consuming my thoughts for so long, but I had not considered the possibility of being in a relationship with him, let alone thought about how I would respond if the option arose. On an unconscious level, I probably knew that it was only the fantasy I desired and not the reality. It was the first time I had felt such strong emotions, and I had no idea what they meant, let alone how to deal with them. I was beginning to feel out of control and I effectively had no way of dealing with the situation. To make matters worse, Steve kept texting me telling me how cute I was and asking to meet again. How could I possibly respond to him when I did know what to say? I had of course, enjoyed getting attention from the man I had been admiring from afar but I couldn't actually be with him, could I?

I had to say something, anything, to keep his interest alive, "I am busy for the rest of the week and not sure when I will be free again". Surprisingly, he did not respond to that message. For some obscure reason, I assumed he would know that I needed time to consider my options and would wait for me in the process. I mean, if he liked me as much as he said he did, then why wouldn't he, right? As it turns out, I could not have been any more wrong.

It was a Saturday night and Clare and I had decided to go to into town for a few drinks after work. The first pub we went to, *The Swan Inn*, was not really our kind of pub (dare I say it was a bit tacky) but it was cheap and a great place to start a pub crawl. As we made our way past the crowds and over to the bar, I immediately spotted Steve sitting at a table with a girl, who was clearly not me. My heart skipped a beat, quite literally, as this was something completely unexpected. We had been on our date just one week before and he had said how much he liked me. My mind was in turmoil: *How can someone move on this quickly? Has he interpreted my message as rejection?* I was upset and confused, desperately trying to decipher the meaning of it all. I excused myself from the bar and went to the bathroom to let out an uncontrollable flow of tears, brought on by the presence of an emotion that I could not describe: possibly jealousy or rage, or both. What I can say for sure, is that my amygdala was in serious overdrive, producing an array of strong emotions I had never felt before.

As I re-entered the bar, I noticed that Steve and his date had fled the premises, leaving an abandoned and insecure little girl in his wake. I immediately texted him, since there was no way I could carry on with the evening without dealing with the issue. I cannot remember exactly what I said but he turned up at the bar an hour later accompanied by one of his work colleagues and more importantly, without his date. Finally, I could breathe again.

I confronted him about the situation and explained that I did have feelings for him, but I didn't know what to do with them. Fortunately, my feelings were reciprocated. After all, he had just sent his date home in a taxi so he could be with me. It was a cruel thing to do admittedly, and all because of me and my inability to let go. But I could justify it in my head: *It's not like I asked him to send his date home, and it is only a first date, I am sure she will get over it quickly. Now wait a minute… Steve and I have only been on one proper date and I am definitely not okay with him dating someone else. What if she has feelings for him like I do? Is it possible that she too could be heartbroken by his cruel and unequivocally unacceptable rejection? Impossible! There is no way she can possibly feel the same way I do, can she? But what do I feel?*

However, I was grateful and relieved, because he had chosen me over someone else. I somehow managed to put my thoughts to one side so I could enjoy his company in yet another different context. I cannot recall what happened for the remainder of the night, but I suspect it was either uneventful or I got too drunk to remember. I can, however, say for certain that we did not sleep together. Regardless of this, my brain was satisfied that we were back on track – whatever that means – and that I had regained control over the situation. Yet another win in my endeavour to be desired by Steve.

The same old questions were replaying in my mind like a broken record stuck on repeat: questions revolving around commitment, relationships, and sexual intercourse. Unsurprisingly, I failed to come up with any answers and reacted with avoidance tactics: one of messages was "Sorry Steve, but I cannot see you for a while. I am not in the right place for dating just now. I do however still like you". See what I did with that response? I cleverly put a hold on our relationship without ending it, hoping he wouldn't lose interest in me. I was under the impression that he would inevitably wait for me. As selfish as it sounds, I think I knew, deep down inside, that I did not want to be with him but equally, I could not stand the thought of not having him in my life. Frustratingly, I could not make sense of my feelings. I could not understand why I did not want to be with him, just as I could not fathom why I needed him in my life: all I knew is that I had to somehow be in control of the situation, in order to retain the status quo in my head. I had developed a dependency on Steve, whereby my identity, my whole being, was embroiled in him and everything he represented in my mind. He had become a fantasy that was dominating my thoughts.

I did not hear from Steve for a few days, then a few days turned into a week. I was beginning to feel restless, but I assumed he was still interested in me, as I was in him. I considered the possibility he was playing it cool and waiting for me to make the next move. After the third week of no communication, I began to question his commitment to me. Feelings of insecurity prompted me to take the initiative and, putting my pride temporarily to one side, I sent him a text, "How are you and are we okay?" In all honesty, I did not care how he was. Actually, that's not strictly true – if he was happy, it would have made me feel uncomfortable and if he was sad, I would have been ecstatic. So yeah, maybe I did care a little, in fact a lot, but certainly not for the right reasons. Really, what I was seeking was confirmation that he was still pining after me. I did not get that confirmation. In fact – much to my amazement – he did not reply at all! *It doesn't make sense! How can he be interested in me one minute, then not the next? Does it have something to do with my text? Have I said something wrong? Perhaps my message lacked clarity? Maybe he needs an explanation as to why I have put our relationship on hold.*

I was beginning to panic as I felt once again like I was losing control over the situation, and over him. Impulsively, I texted him again, asking if he was still talking to me. I waited one day, two days, three days but nothing! Nada! No response whatsoever! I was becoming desperate for a response, so I concocted a plan, one that involved speaking to him face to face. It was a simple plan but it required a great deal of willpower: I would locate and confront him, demanding to know why he had been ignoring me and to discuss the status of our relationship. This way, he would have no option but to respond. Of course, I did consider the possibility that he would reject me, but there was no way I was prepared to let him go, not when I had invested so much time and mental energy into the Steve pursuit. I would appease his worries and in turn obtain control over the situation: this would eradicate my anxieties and enhance my mental well-being.

Saturday morning! I was extremely nervous at the prospect of speaking to Steve, more so than usual given the context in which it would be happening. I scanned the ground floor first before making my way up to the first floor, where my workplace was. There was no sign of him. I wondered briefly if he had a day off, but he was never off on a Saturday. Besides, it was two weeks until Christmas, the centre was much busier than normal, and I very much doubted he would have been granted time off. I considered the possibility that he might have been out the back dealing with shoplifters, or perhaps he was on camera duty. Then I realised he could have been watching me pacing the centre like a woman on a mission, all from behind a lens. My shift was about to start and, as I didn't want to look like a crazy stalker woman, I reverted to plan B – to attract his attention during my shift, when he inevitably walked past the shop. I usually subconsciously counted the number of times he walked past and how often he looked in: the frequency and nature of each encounter would impact on my mood for the rest of the day. These isolated, recurring moments, each of which was unique in its own way, were feeding my addiction and keeping the fantasy alive. On this day, I watched and waited and watched and waited until… there he was, walking past as predicted but again in an unexpected context. He was with a girl and they were holding hands! It was the same girl he had been with on the night I had seen them in the pub! I felt sick to my stomach! Desperately trying to prevent an uncontrollable wave of emotion from erupting from within, I pretended to be engrossed in my work until the coast was clear. Fortunately, I was the only member of staff on the shop floor and this gave me the opportunity to duck down behind the till to compose myself before I resumed my duties.

I had not, up until this point, felt such intense emotions and it was an overwhelming experience. Was I suffering from heartbreak, triggered by unrequited love? I couldn't possibly be in love with him, could I? I had always been successful at managing my emotions, but for some reason, I felt like I had little control over my feelings towards Steve, and no idea how to respond to them. This was a terrifying realisation.

To give you an idea of the level of intensity of my feelings , I would say my emotional response was on a par with the feelings I had experienced during a panic attack I had several years earlier. At least the panic attack had been short-lived, whereas I had a sneaky suspicion that my current emotions would take somewhat longer to diminish. Frustratingly, I did not know what to do or how to deal with the news that Steve had moved on with someone new. I was confused. The pain was so intense that, to avoid having a complete meltdown, I had to force my brain into a different, more positive, mindset.

I considered my options: convince myself that it would be difficult for a while but I would get through it; remember all the times I had witnessed my friends in an emotional state over boys they claimed to have been in love with (and attempted to console them); or attempt to win him back. As I am sure you have already guessed, the obvious answer was the last option: to win him back and risk enduring more pain, but also hope for more pleasure.

I am a girl who puts all her eggs in one basket, and once I have made my mind up about something, I will follow it though, even if I am utterly shit at it. In fact, when I am shit at something, it becomes more of a challenge, to try to become good at it.

A current example of this: I have a target where I must write 2500 words of this book per week. This is about all I can manage, as I work full-time, and have a son and a puppy (recently bought on impulse, the puppy that is... not the son) to take care of. Anything shy of this word count will stress me out and relentlessly gnaw away at my brain so it is just not worth it.

Anyway, I was on a new mission: to prise Steve from his new lover and win him back. May the challenge commence.

University Challenge

My first year of university was, well… better than school anyway. It was compulsory to sign up for two additional subjects to supplement psychology. Without much deliberation, I opted for sociology and anthropology. On my first day at university, a girl who had been in my year at school entered the lecture room and sat next to me. Coincidentally, Sarah also worked in a shop in the centre where I worked, and although we had not spoken at school, I knew her a little from being served in her shop. Based on first impressions I had assumed we were quite different: she had always been a girly girl who was in the popular set. However, it didn't take long for me to realise how wrong I had been. We were so similar! We were both shy, with the same sense of humour: so we bounced off each other well. We also both had crushes on unsuitable men, which we could discuss with each other. How had I not known this girl before? Within a short period of time, we found ourselves socialising outside of university as well.

The first year at university consisted mostly of nights out, with not much studying and the regular last-minute submission of half-finished assignments.

Occasionally, Sarah and I went to university late in the evening with a stash of goodies, and worked on our assignment until 3am in the morning. A true hater of essay writing, I would procrastinate until I had no option but to write so this usually happened just before the deadline. As if finding the relevant text wasn't hard enough, I was expected to write in my own words, and when I did form my own opinions, I was marked down for not referencing them properly. What was I supposed to do? "Reference Francesca Baird, page

222 of my own brain in Francesca's Brain, 2002"? If all I was required to do was regurgitate what I had read then great, that was right up my street. However, this would be deemed to be plagiarism and would inevitably result in a fail. I could not win. Just because someone cannot put something in their own words, it does not necessarily mean that they do not understand the text, right?

There's another reason I hated essay writing: I could easily spend up to an hour or so on a couple of sentences, trying desperately to make the wording less child-like and to construct sentences that were both legible and concise, an almost impossible task (especially within the time frame I had assigned to the work). I would often spend so much time on the first paragraph that I would only have left myself a couple of hours or so to string together the rest of the essay. Don't even get me started on the difficulty I had in highlighting and pulling out parts of the book that were relevant to the question: I would often go round in circles before settling on something that might or might not have been relevant. Finally, there was the structure – knowing which bits go where and linking it all together in a coherent manner… enough said.

If only I had known all this before I started, I would have studied something else or avoided university completely. Regardless of these problems, I always did enough to pass. Interestingly, the best mark I ever achieved was for an anthropology essay I had started at 9am on the day it was due to be submitted. I researched and wrote simultaneously for two and a half hours before pulling everything together to form some sort of conclusion, ready for submission five minutes before the deadline. I suspect the pressure from having a looming deadline prevented me from getting inside my head, and allowed for information to flow more easily that it would have if I had I given myself more time.

Sarah and I were joined at the hip, so now I had an accomplice to help me win Steve back.

We went out five, sometimes six nights a week and I drank, on average, 50 single shot vodka mixers per week. My school friend, Alana, would also join us on the nights that her boyfriend was working as a DJ in the club we often went to: usually a Friday or Saturday. Sunday was a more subdued affair, with the consumption of soft drinks only and a more casual look. The comfort obtained by wearing jeans and a hoody replaced the effects of alcohol and helped to enhance my confidence on the night. Every day, we would formulate a plan for the night ahead, which was mainly focused on logistics. A typical plan started with a quick session in the student bar to pre-load on cheap drinks before moving on to a more expensive but more atmospheric pub for one or two more. Usually tipsy by this point, we would head to club number one (where Sarah's love interest worked), followed by an equal stint at club number two (Steve's place of work). This compromise (the 50/50 split of our time) ensured that we both had the opportunity to make ourselves visibly noticeable by our love interest. Admittedly, it rarely worked out this way, since we were each reluctant to leave the venue where our respective men worked. Alana's priority was to have a good night out with the girls, and so she was always happy to go with flow.

Our nights out usually ended in one of two ways. Sometimes, we would be ecstatic at how the night's events had unfolded, because of who had been on duty at the venues that night. In that case, we would share our happiness by singing our own rendition of "Maggie May" by Rod Stewart or Take That's "Never Forget" at the top of our lungs while walking home at 3am, or 6am on the occasions when we went to the Casino for an early breakfast. Alternatively, the nights would end in tears. In that case, we would walk back to Sarah or Alana's place (since they both lived within walking distance of the clubs) contemplating what had gone wrong, with our tails between our legs. When we got there, we would have a pick-me-up cheese and coleslaw sandwich followed by a good old bedtime sob (or at least this is my recollection of how the typical night ended).

I have some deeply fond memories of my nights out with Sarah and Alana. The best nights were often the ones where we made little effort and had low expectations. Our lifestyle was expensive and most of our student loans went on outfits to be worn on nights out. We could not possibly be seen wearing the same outfit more than once, unless of course a good period of time (say six months) had elapsed. As a lover of denim jeans, it was simple as all I needed for every occasion was a new top to match my jeans. There was also the opportunity to mix and match previously worn outfits or add an accessory to create a different look. This was a great solution in times of financial difficulty, when my student loan had miraculously disappeared, and the credit card was maxed. In an attempt to be frugal, we bought cheap bottles of vodka and hid them in our bags, to be brought out and consumed in the more expensive bars and nightclubs. It must have seemed odd to the bartender when two drunk girls ordered two glasses of diet coke then rushed off to the toilets with them. I recall one instance, where the non-alcoholic to alcoholic drink conversion took place in the disabled toilet of our regular nightclub. We were sitting on the floor, precariously pouring vodka straight out the bottle and into our half empty glasses of coke at a ratio of 1:1 when the door swung open and exposed us to everyone outside the cubicle, including one of the bartenders who was on shift that night. Unsure how to react having been caught out, we just smiled politely, shut the door and carried on pouring.

Sarah and I had many a laugh reminiscing about our nights out and our silly antics. We often discussed them over a large portion lunch at *Hungry Horse* (a pub within a short drive of the university).

Alana was studying at a different University and therefore, she did not partake in our lunch time discussions. Our conversations about the nights that ended in tears would include a summary of what we thought had gone wrong and how we could redeem ourselves on our next night out. The tears were a reaction to several things, namely, "our men" not being on duty as anticipated, or a perceived lack of attention by our men. Any attempt at dialogue would be discussed in depth with every word pulled apart and analysed for subjective meaning – how would Steve have interpreted "I still like you?" Did I say it in a jokey way (letting him know I was still interested but not desperate) or a serious way (the true meaning, which was "I need you and I will do whatever it takes to get you back")? If I could not convince myself that it had been interpreted a joke, then I would make plans to correct his assumptions on our next night out. I had to ensure that he remained oblivious to my obsession, since this would inevitably scare him away and scupper my chances of winning him back.

My obsession with Steve continued throughout the first three years at university. I hardly spoke to him during this time, but I saw him, or rather he saw me, on nights out. In the early stages, just seeing him was enough to fulfil my desire. However, my infatuation had moved up a gear or two since our relationship had briefly developed. I felt a pressing desire to take back control, to seek confirmation that he was still interested in me, thus satisfying my brain's requirement for equilibrium. The thought of not having him in my life was simply unimaginable. He was not only my security and safety net, but he was also protecting me from the ambiguous, scary and ever-changing world that existed outside my own head. Of course, there was always the option of transferring my obsession to another man, possibly even an attainable one. As I received a lot of male attention on my nights out, some might argue that it would have been an easy swap. If only it had been that simple. I don't know if I made a conscious effort not to let anyone else in or if I was simply incapable of doing so, but my mind was set on Steve, and Steve only. It was a losing battle for men who liked the "hard to get" approach to dating.

In this period, it became increasingly difficult for me to regulate my emotions. The alcohol and lack of sleep exacerbated the problem and I began to feel stuck in a vicious cycle, drinking at night and obsessing over Steve during the day. Everything in my life centred on Steve and nothing else held any significance. Frighteningly, it felt like my sense of identity was being threatened by a darker, self-centred, and angrier version of me. As a child, I had been a sensitive, sensible girl who cared deeply for others and did not get caught up in situations that were not good for me (apart from the time I tried to smoke paper and almost set my house on fire... but that had been a one-off). Somewhere along the line, I had lost myself, my true self being replaced by a superficial person, who I was ashamed of. I so badly wanted to revert to the kinder, softer, less self-obsessed version of me but like any addiction, a part of me craved an emotional reaction: and it was that reaction that was induced by Steve and the circumstances in which my dependency was unfolding.

Exhausted from being me, I wanted to escape, just for a while, to give me some much needed time to recuperate. I had an increasing desire to isolate myself and escape human contact. Alongside this, I developed a pattern of waking up feeling overwhelmed by negative emotions and, without the mental strength to retaliate, I surrendered by running away from everything and everyone. I stopped attending lectures and I even took a day off work, which I never usually did. Without the words to explain myself, I avoided the situation completely by failing to call in or answer my manager's call, inevitably making matters worse. My mum tried a whole range of approaches to get me out of bed and out of my current state. To begin with, she spoke words of encouragement: "You can do this. You just need to be strong". Then, out of worry and increased frustration at my lack of response, she tried the guilt trip tactic: "You cannot let people down, they need you and there is no time for them to get someone else". When that wasn't successful, she retorted: "Get out of bed now or I will drag you out!"

Her attempts did of course falter as she realised that there was nothing she, or anyone else could do to motivate me. A couple of hours later, when the dust had settled and my mum had calmed down, I hesitantly called my work to explain and grovel for forgiveness. Fortunately, they were very understanding and appeared to be genuinely concerned for my well-being. I went back to work the following day, nervous, but in a better headspace for tackling my issues (whatever they were).

Unfortunately, this newly formed pattern of negative thoughts and avoidant behaviour continued. Increasingly, I found myself desperate to escape everything and everyone and unable to face a world outside my head. I no longer believe Steve was the sole cause of my emotional state: it's more likely he was simply the symptom of a deeper, psychological problem.

On one occasion, when I was feeling low but had forced myself to get out of bed and catch the bus into work, I couldn't cope, so I got off of the bus and caught another one heading in the opposite direction towards home. The mere thought of social interaction was mentally taxing and anxiety-provoking, to the point that avoidance felt like my only option. This tactic helped me remove the pressure and relieved my mind from intrusive thoughts, albeit temporarily. In these moments, all the worry and anxiety evaporated and was replaced by fatigue and a relentless desire to escape real life through sleep. Returning to work the day after was always easier as I had prepared myself mentally for the challenge of explaining myself to my curious and concerned boss. On reflection, it seems strange that I was sometimes unable to go to work when my external stressors were relatively low and I was unable to identify a definitive cause for my anxiety and subsequent escapist behaviour. On the contrary, I generally managed to get up and go to work when I had real issues to worry about – such as the need to provide a face-to-face explanation for my absence (with the knowledge that I had let people down). Yet somehow – and this is a recurring theme in my life –I seem to be better at managing difficult situations when the issue is very apparent and can be directly attributed to feelings of stress or anxiety.

I am not entirely sure why this is but, as a lifetime sufferer of anxiety, I can only conclude that it has something to do with an underlying need to feel anxious. "Normal life" scares me, as I often question the meaning of the mundane day-to-day routine: *so this is it and then we die*. My frustratingly overactive brain must find a reason to feel anxious and, if there isn't one, I will create a drama to bring about this effect. I will come back to this point later but before I move on, I want to apologise if anything I have said up until this point has left you perplexed, thinking, "what on earth is this girl on?" Hell, I struggle to understand what goes on in my head and I have been self-analysing the workings of my brain for my entire life. However, I do think it is important for me to pick apart my thought processes to offer you some insight into the workings of my brain. And, when all is said and done, there is also the fact that it is both liberating and therapeutic for me to write it all down.

Jumping Jobs

During my third year at university, I became increasingly anxious and my mental health began to deteriorate. This was not helped by my dislike for tutorials, which came with high expectations, we were expected to have knowledge of specific topics and to form our own opinions to share with fellow students. I had no knowledge (probably through lack of studying) and no opinion on anything other than Steve. I also felt incredibly uncomfortable speaking to dedicated, confident students, who all seemed to be able to successfully form opinions and articulate their views. To make matters worse, *The Natural World* was under new management. Without my confidantes there to look after me, there was no longer that feeling of unity and belonging that I had once had. My identity was weakening and in need of support. I did not know who to turn to next. My family did not understand what was happening to me (or maybe it was more that I could not express it to them). I began to take more and more days off work, until it reached the point where – through unbearable guilt and depression – I left my job on a whim and without working my notice period. When I looked back on my decision, I soon realised the error of my ways, primarily the negative impact it had had on my mental health. I had made a huge mistake and the impact was immeasurable. Steve was still working as a security guard in the centre and I was still attached to him… to the centre… to my work… to all of it. So why on earth had I left a job that brought me closer to the things that made me feel secure?

It was obvious that I had developed a dependency on Steve (in case you hadn't worked that one out yet) and everything that

I linked to him. It was only after such an irrational decision that I could finally acknowledge not only the intensity of my desires, but also my need to control my environment. By leaving my job, I had lost a part of my identity and this made me feel confused, frustrated, agitated and, above all, anxious. I felt I was at risk of having a mental breakdown, so I had to find a way to relieve my anxiety, but how? What could I do to make me feel safe and secure again? What made me feel safe? Well, there was Steve and work and er… Steve and work. Nothing else. To me, there was only one possible solution: I would get another job in the centre. *Now, which shop has a vacancy?* The jewellery shop on the ground floor of the centre, here we come.

My first day at my new job was nothing short of horrific. Far from what I had envisaged, it was small, bright and much busier than *The Natural World*. The windows at either side of the entrance were filled with jewellery and I had limited visibility of the centre. The only view available was a *Sky* stall in the middle of the centre, and skinny strips of a clothing shop at either side of the stall. *How can I possibly watch Steve from this angle? Where is the large open space, offering a panoramic view of the centre and Steve as he walks from one end of the centre to the other? Where are the moving stairs with glass mirrors on either side, reflecting the lower level and Steve as he approaches the stairs? Hang on, this is the lower level of the centre. No, it can't be. It feels so different. Is this even the centre, my centre that I know and love? Something isn't right.*

It felt like I was on a different planet. Even the snapshot I had of Steve as he walked past was somehow tarnished by my location, as if seeing him in a different context somehow made him different. I was different. To say that I was panicking is a complete understatement. I was overwhelmed and deeply confused by my new environment. Then there were my colleagues to consider: *Who are these strange people? What do I know about them? What do they know about me?*

I suspect they thought of me as competent and reliable, and I was, or at least I did have the potential to be these things. To even try to begin to explain my feelings at this early stage in the game seemed futile. If only they had known the real me, they would have known that I was a fraud, pretending to be stable to get the job, when inside I was screaming, desperately craving a level of support that you should not expect from a boss: nor is it possible to obtain that level of support without developing an attachment with that person first. If I had told them about my issues during the interview, then I would not have got the job, but I had to work. I needed the income to sustain the lifestyle I was accustomed to (drink and Steve) and to prevent my mum from killing me. You see my dilemma?

I successfully completed my first week in my new job without crying (in front of anyone) and with 100% attendance. Top marks for deceiving the staff by pretending to be something I was not. Let's be honest, they obviously thought that I had potential, and they were considering me as an eventual candidate for the supervisor role. I am saying this not because of my ego, but based on experience and the positive feedback I have received over the years. Of course, I could be wrong in my assessment of others assessment of me, but it seems un-likely. People say what they mean, right? And what people say is that I am determined, hard-working and intelligent (intelligent – yeah right). Little do they know I am like a ticking timebomb, ready to ex-plode, with complete disregard for those affected by my behaviour.

After my first few weeks in my new role, the initial "I can do this" stage had expired. My feelings of panic from starting a new role and wanting to impress, were replaced by feelings of loss, sadness and mental exhaustion. I had worked so hard to fight my feelings and preserve my position in my new job, really I had. However, I had to ask myself if it was all worth it when it was causing me so much internal pain.

I was certainly not comfortable in my environment, working with strangers and serving people who spend a ridiculous amount on generic pieces of jewellery. I would literally spend hours helping someone choose an engagement ring with a tiny little stone that could hardly be seen with the naked eye. "When are you getting married?", I would ask. *Two years in July! Holy smoke, they probably won't even be together in two years' time! Why are they wasting their time and money on this inadequate run of the mill, piece of... diamond ring* (of course I knew not to say this out loud, but it didn't stop me from thinking it). Perhaps I was just jealous because no one had ever bought me an expensive piece of jewellery.

The job was monotonous and completely unconnected to my interests, but there was one positive... I got to wear a suit to work. *Professional Fran, here I come!* Oh, how looks can be deceiving. It is not like Steve had much opportunity to see me in my suit. The restricted, infrequent Steve moments – which felt like spotting one of the Big Five – were far from rewarding. In the wrong context, my feelings were somehow dissociated from Steve, as if I couldn't any longer feel anything for him in that specific context. Seeing him just reinforced what I had lost and how far away I was from fulfilling my desires.

Unsurprisingly, it didn't take long until the whole "I can't go to work" habit kicked in again. However, as I hadn't had time to develop a relationship with my colleagues, it was much harder for me to rectify the situation after I had missed a day's work. Moreover, I did not have the energy or motivation to explain my difficulties in the hope of gaining their support and understanding. Unable to feel safe in my new environment, I couldn't even begin to contemplate a situation that would make me feel comfortable and evoke the same positive emotions I had had when I worked in *The Natural World* and had first developed my interest in Steve.

I was beginning to realise that my attempts to reinstate what I had once had were futile – it would never be the same again, irrespective of where I worked or how my relationship developed with Steve. This idea scared the hell out of me: I was not prepared to live an anxiety-driven life, devoid of meaning and happiness. As the pain of the reality was far too intense to accept, I chose instead to venture down the most desirable and less destructive route of escapism, by convincing myself that I could get back what I had lost. I just had to find a job in another shop in the centre that would suit me better and provide a more optimal view of Steve.

I left my job at the jewellers without notice. A few days in bed gave me sufficient time to recuperate and once again pick myself up from a depressed state to an "I can do this, time to fight back" mind frame. Up I got and off I went… to the centre, in search of another, more suitable job role. I must have spent around an hour wandering aimlessly, searching for vacancies that had ceased to exist. Much to my disappointment, the only vacancy was in the store where Steve's new girlfriend worked… well even I knew that would have been a disaster in the making.

In complete disarray, I ventured to the next nearest shopping centre in the hope of finding the next best thing. Miss Selfridge had a part-time job vacancy with hours that would fit in with university and allow for a short walk to and from the old centre on my lunch break. I didn't have a clue about fashion, but I was used to working with the public and I knew how to sell. How hard could it be?

With my options running low, I applied for the position and had my induction a few days later.

I was initially apprehensive due to all the usual questions circulating around my head, as if it was for the first time. However, one positive I chose to focus on was the lack of a distinctive uniform. Without this to give away my place of work, Steve would surely wonder where I was employed. Perhaps curiosity and intrigue would even prompt him to communicate with me. My colleagues were fashion-conscious, the store itself was much bigger, had music playing continually, and the team was larger than I had expected. This was not what I was used to: I was completely out of my depth. Despite my ability to play to the audience, I was concerned that my internal struggles would, at some stage, permeate their way to the surface and reveal my fragility.

Having spent the first morning completing forms and watching short videos about the company ethos and all that malarkey, I was asked to change into the work clothes. I was handed a pink, low-cut T-shirt made of an extremely thin material. I went into the changing rooms to embrace my new look when… oh shit… I realised I had forgotten to put a bloody bra on! This might not have been such a big issue had I started the job when I had just turned 16, but I was 17 now and experiencing the changes to my body that accompany growth and development in young adulthood. I remained petite but my boobs, almost overnight, had strangely transformed my figure into a womanly, perhaps even sexually appealing frame. Not wearing a bra was something I would not, could not consider… not deliberately anyway. How had this happened? I had been trying on a new top without a bra and somehow forgotten to take it off again to put on the layers beneath – don't ask! It was the unusual sequence of events that had thrown me, of course, and prevented me from getting dressed properly.

Even more amazingly, I had not realised my mistake until I was asked to change my top. How I hadn't noticed this anomaly is still a mystery. Without the option of going back in time and redressing myself, I had yet another one of those "consider my options" moments: I could wear the top and have my assets on show (and given that the top was literally see through, I might as well have been topless); I could confess to the errors of my ways and buy a bra before I resumed my role; OR I could run away and get a job in another shop. You might be surprised that the latter option was not my chosen course of action on this occasion. After all, this would seem to have been the most likely outcome given my past behaviour in response to anxiety-provoking events.

Let's just say that for someone who likes predictability, I can be very unpredictable. Cast your mind back to what I said about coping better in challenging situations and less well when things become the norm: well this is just another example of this. The upshot was that option two triumphed. Sheepishly, I confessed to the shift supervisor and she reassured me by telling me that many women do this on occasion. I explained it wasn't deliberate and she gave me permission to go and purchase a new bra before starting my shift. So off I went on my expedition to locate Steve… ahem, I mean a correct fitting bra (hard to come by) and when I returned, normal work resumed without further mention of the forgotten bra.

Now everyone knows that people with autism are straight talking and tend to be honest, right? Well, from my perspective of how I function, I do and I don't agree with this. I undoubtedly say it like it is and have always considered myself as honest. I have never really understood people who tell little white lies. I mean, what is the point in that? If you are going to tell a lie, you might as well go big! However – and I will come back to this later – there are situations in which I have not been completely honest and so I guess I could be considered a hypocrite (note that, even though I am the one saying this, I don't actually believe I am). I would never want to hurt someone with my words and will always try to refrain from saying something I would deem to be hurtful, even if it means avoiding the truth. However, I cannot promise that my non-verbal communication would follow suit. Equally, I would never say that someone looked lovely if they looked bloody awful, as that would involve making a conscious effort to go out of my way to lie and would make me feel extremely uncomfortable.

Having said all this, I do recall an awkward moment when I said something inappropriate and brutally honest in front of a customer during one of my shifts at Miss Selfridge. The customer asked me where a top that was displayed on a mannequin could be found in the shop. While standing beside the customer, I shouted to a colleague at the other end of the store: "Rach! You know that top… the really ugly one on the mannequin, where is it?" Rachel ignored my request: in fact she ran into the changing room to escape the embarrassing situation, leaving me to locate the top and confront the customer with it. Needless to say, the customer did not make a purchase and we lost the sale.

However, usually I have a remarkable way of making people like me, particularly the older generation who want to protect and look after me. I would describe myself as open and someone who shows no hesitation in revealing my flaws and insecurities – part of the reason, I suspect, why I appear vulnerable. People have often described me as witty, capable, and intelligent – a review I agree with, albeit only on a superficial level, since my inner failings are nicely tucked away from society's view. My boss at Miss Selfridge liked me. She was aware of my struggles (at least the parts I was prepared to show her) and was more than willing to support me. Either that, or she felt that she had a duty to support her staff. I was quite happy for someone older, in a position of authority and with an abundance of life experience, to take me under her wing and look out for my well-being. Our relationship was, however, short lived as she resigned a few months after I started working there. Apparently, she had been offered a managerial position for another retail clothing company, not too dissimilar to the one we worked for.

I could not get my head around this situation. She had seemed happy in her role. Fortunately, I had not been there long enough to form an attachment and, although I could not fathom her resolve to move, I somehow managed to adjust to the uncontrollable change and come out the other end, relatively unscathed.

Searching For Answers

As I've mentioned, my third year at university was arduous, more so than the previous two years, and not only because of the learning material or workload. The truth is, I had lost all interest in my studies. This was partly because of Steve, but mostly because I had realised that my studies were not going to help me understand myself as I had anticipated – the structure of learning a little about a wide range of topics was doing little to support my endeavour.

If only there had been the option to study a specialised degree, or one that was tailored to my individual needs and questions, pre-defined by me. My true goal was to find answers related to me and how I function. I wasn't really interested in the wider population. I was finding life difficult and I desperately needed answers. I wanted to know why I developed particular obsessions, and I wanted to understand my rigid, inflexible thinking patterns. I also wanted to know if I had an underlying predisposition to anxiety and I wanted to understand whether my issues were biological or environmentally defined.

This would have been far more useful in helping me understand myself. By laying down the foundations of who I am (in my core being), I would have been in a better position to move forward and achieve a more fulfilling life. Arguably, therapy might have offered the answers to such questions, but my experience suggests otherwise: possibly because of a lack of understanding of autism in females in myself and health professionals alike.

The way that Steve had become the centre of my focus also left me with very little time or mental capacity to engage with my studies. I had become increasingly distracted by my thoughts (restricted and obsessive thoughts about him) and subsequent emotions: fear, lust, depression, anxiety, and possibly even love (?). There was an overwhelming fear of losing control, losing my identity and of not having Steve present in my life. Perhaps, if Steve had had a degree in psychology or had at least shown an interest in the subject, I would have been more committed to my studies. The truth was far from it: Steve's world was far from the realms of academia. He was a commendable hard grafter, but definitely not the academic type.

Up until this point, I had managed to do the bare minimum and pass my exams while keeping my fantasy about Steve alive and continuing to have an active nightlife.

On the night before my third-year exam, I can distinctly recall sitting at the living room table, papers everywhere, thinking that I had not done enough studying. It was 11pm and I was feeling depressed, desperate to go to bed and sleep through the exam. I did not have the mental courage or strength to pull me through it and I simply could not envisage an outcome that would make it all worthwhile. Passing my exam would have been nice and, it would have changed how I felt for a couple of minutes, but I knew it wouldn't relieve me of my mental turmoil and transform my life for the better. As I was void of positive thoughts about Steve, I did not have the desire or motivation to stay up, studying, all night. I just wanted to run away from everything and everyone, and that is exactly what I did. I went to my bed with the notion that I would see how I felt in the morning before making my decision about whether to attend the exam or not.

I woke up the following morning, unable to move due to anxiety and depression. The mere thought of getting out of my bed was unbearable at best, and excruciatingly mentally debilitating at worst. In desperation to escape my life, and with a growing certainty that I would fail my exam anyway, I reached what seemed like the only sensible conclusion – not to sit the exam and to leave university.

I did say that I don't make life easy for myself – this represented three years of studying being thrown away in one irrational but also a very real, anxiety-driven, moment. In one last-ditch attempt to re-deem myself and continue with my studies, I did in fact pay to attend the resit exams. I was fully aware that this was my last opportunity to continue with my studies and I was determined to overcome this battle – even a three-year designated degree was better than nothing. I could sit the exam then retreat into myself again until I could find a way, the right way, to move forward.

Right, okay, lets do this. I am feeling positive. I have this one in the bag, right? Wrong? I cannot do this and I am too depressed to get out of bed. I allowed the negative thoughts to sweep through my mind and as I didn't have the willpower to change my mindset, I took the easy option of escapism with yet another glorious day in bed. That was the end of the road for me as a student at *Aberdeen University*. I could not help but feel annoyed with my emotionally fuelled over-active mind for having failed me once again.

I left my job at Miss Selfridge without handing in my notice and on a whim… blah blah… you know the drill by now. Not only had I left university, but I was jobless too and for reasons that should have been within my control. My mother, who was understandably frustrated by my inability to cope with normal life, would switch between "That's a shame, love" to "You need help but I cannot support you forever. You must learn to stand on your own two feet and be-come financially independent. You just need to get on with it like the rest of us do!"

She wasn't telling me anything I didn't already know. What I know I should be doing and what I actually do are two very sepa-rate and often opposing things. It's not like I wanted to be jobless and without any qualifications. Over the years I have come to realise how my brain works: the unconscious part of my brain makes the decisions and dictates my behaviour, irrespective of what I know I should be doing; the conscious part of my brain (the tip of the iceberg) simply responds to its superior, the unconscious mind. Everyone who has suffered difficulties or supported someone going through a difficult time will be well aware that telling someone to "get on with it" is possibly the worst thing you can say and that it is bound to have the opposite effect to what you intended.

Although I can completely understand why my mother said what she said – and the frustration and worry that led to it – and while I agree that yes, sometimes people do need a kick up the arse – there is often an underlying (often unknown) cause for un-expected and unintentional behaviour, whereby their behaviour is an expression of their emotions, which require an immediate outlet.

I am a strong believer in the idea that "bad" behaviour is often a cry for help, for support to help a person to understand and over-come their challenges, in a way that might ultimately change their behaviour for the better. Telling someone who is struggling to get on with it is guaranteed to make them feel isolated and less likely to seek support from the person giving them this advice.

Of course, it's not always easy for the person giving support (especially close relatives) to respond in a positive way since they themselves are feeling frustrated, and possibly even angry with the individual in question. My mother, who is impulsive and emo-tionally volatile, understandably transitioned from being kind and reassuring to being angry and frustrated with my behaviour. Why? Because she cared and was deeply concerned about my well-being. She did her best for me and has always put her children first. She may not always go about things the right way; but then again who does? I certainly don't.

Perhaps my mum did get it right when she gave me the perfect ultimatum: go and find a job or seek professional help or you will have to move out. Losing my only safety net would have been unthinkable, so I called the doctor and booked an appointment right away. I had little faith in the system, so I was sceptical about seeing someone, but I had no other choice. It wasn't therapy per se I was looking for, as I didn't know if I wanted to or needed to change. What I wanted was for someone to say "This is how your brain functions and this is why you are different" – ultimately, I wanted to be labelled. Now I know this may be controversial and it may even appear as if I was looking for an excuse for my behaviour. Furthermore, some people may believe that labels are irrelevant and that I should instead have been trying to find a mechanism or tool for dealing with my issues in a bid to overcome them.

While I agree, to some extent, with both of these points (that I should look at ways of addressing my issues, and that I was looking for a reason to explain my behaviour), I do also feel that a label would have helped me understand myself and would have been the first step in finding the right support for me. There is also the notion that, if you are labelled, the diagnosis becomes a defining feature of who you are, and that highlighting my differences with the general population would only serve to further isolate me from the rest of society. Yet somehow, at that time in my life (pre-diagnosis), I could not have felt any more alone. Why? Because I knew I was different, but I did not know why. Yet, I was made to feel by others that I ought to be the same as everyone else. Under pressure to conform, I suppressed my true self, whatever that was. Can you imagine how incredibly exhausted and detached from society I felt?

Yes, I knew I had to make changes to my life and find solutions to manage situations effectively, but there were unresolved issues, deeply embedded within me. For me to move forward, I had to understand these issues and not suppress them. This is what I was hoping to achieve when the doctor referred me to see a psychiatrist.

Although I felt I was taking positive actions in some areas of my life, my obsession with Steve remained. At one point, I discovered he had resigned from his role as security guard in the centre. Despite trying my hardest to think rationally, I could not take my mind off him. I was over the moon to find that my mum was working in *John Lewis* and knew of his whereabouts. He was now employed in the same store as her and this was fortunately linked to the centre via a skywalk. I decided that I had to secure a job alongside him. This would surely bring me even closer to him than I had ever been, as we would actually be working in the same store. I would be able to see him every day and this more than made up for the fact it would partially be outside the shopping centre: the centre itself still meant a lot to me and it was a negative not to be working there. I quickly dismissed any thoughts that my behaviour might be similar to that of a stalker.

Unfortunately, the process of obtaining a job was not as easy as I had anticipated. *John Lewis* is one of those high-end retailers that won't just give you a job because of who you know. If you want to become a JL partner, you have to go through a rigorous, lengthy interview involving group work and hypothetical questions such as what you would take to a desert island if you were only allowed three items. At the time I thought the answers mattered but now I realise that they just wanted to see how well interviewees worked as part of a group. I obviously did well in this respect, as there were only a few of us employed out of a substantial group. I was allocated a role as a *John Lewis* partner (basically just a sales assistant) in the station-ery department. I didn't find it an enjoyable place to work. There was no atmosphere whatsoever and, as a prerequisite to working for a prestigious company, everyone had to take themselves very seriously. It was unfortunate that my mum worked in the clothing department, floors apart, as she would have made my experience working for the company much more enjoyable.

On my first day, I mentioned to one of my colleagues that my mother Doreen also worked in the store. They replied: "Oh right, Doreen… hmmm… which department does she work in?" I explained that she worked in the clothing department, had short hair and was quite eccentric. "Ah you mean Rosa". Typically for my mother, she had decided one day that she was bored of being Doreen so she had approached HR and asked them to change her name to Rosa. Of course, they took her request very seriously. She had received a new name badge and her colleagues had been instructed to call her Rosa from there on in. It took a bit of getting used to (especially since I had never heard her mention that name before) but over time, I did manage to switch from calling her Doreen to Rosa… in the workplace only.

Possibly the most entertaining shift I had was when my mum offered to cover a shift in my department. It was approaching Christmas and a customer was purchasing a gift tag. My mum pulled out a long plastic bag, designed to hold rolls of wrapping paper and then… weeeeeee… the tiny gift tag went straight to the bottom of the bag. The customer just looked at her strangely as she handed over the inappropriately sized bag. The following customer had three items to purchase, one of which my mother hid below the till to confuse the customer. They said: "Erm, where is the pen I am purchasing? There are only two items in the bag and there should be three". My mum just replied with "No, you only gave me two items, I am afraid you must be mistaken".

I didn't see much of Steve during my time working at *John Lewis*. He was on camera duty for most of the time and infrequently visited the shop floor. Despite working in close-ish proximity to him, I felt uncomfortable in my surroundings and it was beginning to impact on my feelings towards my home life too. My identity – which, as we all know by now, is inextricably linked with my environment – was weakening. I was losing my core identity, my anchor, the thing that is supposed to hold me together during a crisis. Like a piece of driftwood floating in the sea, I had no direction or purpose. I felt frightened and vulnerable, desperately clinging on to something that made me feel safe and secure in a terrifyingly ambiguous world, and that something was still Steve.

Meanwhile, I was contending with my initial psychiatric assessment. This included the usual checklist of questions. For example, "Have you ever thought about killing yourself?" Well who hasn't? But that doesn't mean I would actually do it. I will rate this two out of ten. "Do you see things that are not there?" No, I will rate this one out of five. "Do you spend excessive amounts of money?" Well it depends… is there a value that constitutes excessive and what is the timescale for spending this money? I will give this two out of five. I hate rating scale questionnaires as a tool for diagnosis – surely an individual's answer will depend on the context in which the question is understood and thus the answer is open to interpretation? Yet there must be a reason why health practitioners use this method to assist with their diagnostic assessment. Excuse my negativity towards these types of questionnaires but I get frustrated with everything that is not black and white. I do nonetheless think there is some value in what I am saying. Everyone is unique. Given the complexity of the brain, a "one size fits all" approach is surely not the best mechanism for understanding an individual's challenges and determining the level of support required? Perhaps this explains why rating scales are often used in conjunction with other methods for diagnosis, as they do not provide enough information on their own.

In any case, the answers I provided were clearly sufficient to allow the psychiatrist to reach his verdict. He informed me that he did not think that I had a mental health disorder that requires medication (such as bipolar disorder or schizophrenia). He did however say that he thought I had a borderline personality disorder but that there was nothing he could do to help me (in other words, he couldn't write me a prescription). He advised me that cognitive behavioural therapy might be the best course of action and offered to refer me to see a psychologist.

From what little I knew about CBT at that time, I must admit that I was dubious of the support on offer. But I didn't have anything to lose either, so I accepted his proposal. When I left the assessment centre, I immediately researched borderline personality disorder on my phone – it implies a person who tends to have disturbed ways of thinking, impulsive behaviour, a distorted sense of self and problems controlling their emotions. They may have intense but unstable relationships and a tendency to worry about people abandoning them. My initial thoughts were that it accurately described some aspects of my personality. Now let's look at the causes – genetics, problems with brain development and or environmental… ah ha, the good old nature versus nurture debate. So basically, the cause is unknown. The recommended treatment…? Psychotherapy – to help people get a better sense of control over their thoughts and feelings.

Upon reflection, I was disappointed with the outcome of my assessment. Something about the diagnosis did not add up. It did not seem to account for all aspects of me, such as my restricted, repetitive thoughts. Furthermore, the term itself created negative connotations in my mind, since my personality is a fundamental part of who I am. What was the psychologist saying? That I was the issue? Was there something inherently wrong with my actual personality?

This notion, that I was somehow responsible for my problems, did not sit comfortably with me at all. To be honest, I would have preferred it if I had been told that my brain processed things in an irregular way and required drugs to promote healthy brain functioning. At least that way, I could have dissociated myself from the diagnosis and retained the positive aspects of myself.

What about my anxiety? Where did this fit into my diagnosis? My anxiety and repetitive thoughts were, at times, so debilitating and disruptive to my daily functioning that I had convinced myself that I had a serious mental health illness. I can think of a couple of examples that help to portray the intensity of my anxiety and how it can affect me…

The first is a distinct memory from my childhood. I was in the car, on my way back from visiting our family in Glasgow. My dad was driving, while my mum was up front in the passenger seat. My sister, brother and I were squeezed in the back. In an attempt to avoid the traffic, we were driving late at night, in the dark, which is unfortunate as my anxiety is always more pronounced in the evening for some reason. We must have been approximately an hour and a half into the journey, roughly halfway between Glasgow and Aberdeen, and I was looking out of the window into nothingness, processing my thoughts. I was deliberating about where I had been and where I was heading for, quite literally. The upheaval of a change to my environment and routine was significant to the point where it required in depth processing. First there was the immediate past to consider: I had become accustomed to my environment and had enjoyed spending time with my grandparents and cousins, who were of a similar age to me. We only visited Glasgow once or twice a year and I was struggling to understand how we could see so little of our close family members.

I remember thinking about how much I would miss them. When would we see them again? Why was everyone else so accepting of this? Even though I knew we would see them again – unless of course I died – it all just seemed so final. How could we spend two whole weeks with the same people and then not see them again for months? It was nonsensical: it required a great deal of mental adjustment for me to get my head around it. Then I considered where we were physically at that moment in time. We were in limbo. We were no longer with family but not at home either. We were in between different realms, and I had no control over the situation.

Finally, my mind focused on the immediate and unavoidable future. Where were we going? Home. I should have been excited, right? No! I was aware that my home would feel strange on my first night back: it would feel like it did not belong to me. I knew this from my previous experiences of returning home after being away for a period of time. The transition was so great that my identity was temporarily lost.

As my thoughts began to spiral out of control, I tried to muster the strength to remain calm but with all the uncertainty and weakening sense of identity, my efforts remained futile. Then the most anxiety-provoking thought entered my mind: going back to school on Monday!

Oh fuck! I couldn't breathe! School makes me anxious: I hate school! Wait, I can't actually breathe and I am not exaggerating this time! Fuck, I am dying! This is it! My biggest fear is finally upon me! Mum, Dad, take me to the nearest hospital now!

Tears were running down my face and I was extremely distressed, unable to breathe and screaming for my dad to take me to hospital – overt symptoms which meant that they had to take me seriously this time. My dad responded promptly but not in the way I had expected. He stopped the car at the side of the motorway.

"There is no hospital around here", I shouted. My heart was racing faster than ever. "You need air", he said, as my mum jumped out the front passenger door and opened my door.

How the fuck is the fresh air going to save me when I am dying?

My entire body was shaking and I could not stand up, so my mum hauled me out of my seat and held me tight, at the side of the motorway and in complete darkness. "You are having a panic attack. You will be alright. Deep breaths. In… out… slowly". This was not something I had experienced before. It all seemed too real to be something that had been created solely by my mind. The physical sensations I was experiencing were certainly real. My mum somehow managed to calm me as she hugged me in the back of the car for the remainder of the journey. Fortunately, I have never had a panic attack of this intensity since.

Another story that highlights the impact of my anxiety comes from a night out in my late teens. It was a typical night out that progressed in the usual fashion – a few drinks in Sarah's flat followed by a pub crawl, a spot of dancing in our favourite nightclub then onto the casino to place a few sneaky bets, followed by breakfast at 3am. I am not entirely sure what triggered my emotional state but I can only assume it had something to do with Steve. Often, when I am on a night out, I can be having a great night, dancing away, when soberness and exhaustion or a combination of both kick in and suddenly I am on a mission for food then bed. This night however, ended very differently. It was not so much the tears (which were common practice), but more the extent of my emotional state and my desire to seek help, instantly. I was fine one minute, then suddenly, without hesitation, I left the casino, got in the nearest taxi and asked the driver to take me to hospital, with Sarah in tow. I told her: "I am so depressed; I cannot cope any more and I need help". Sarah understood. She was my best friend and knew that there was no way she could talk me out of it. It was a case of letting me go on my own or going with me to offer her support.

We sat in A&E waiting room for a good hour, which was ample time for me to sober up and contemplate my decision... what would I say to the doctor? I was depressed and I needed help, pills perhaps. I had tried Prozac and it had driven me completely insane (even more so than normal). What else would they have been able to do? I had thought they could put me in a mental health institution for the night, but now I could not see the benefit in doing so, as I was not a threat to myself or others. Besides, my appointment with the psychologist was approaching. I just needed to be patient and wait.

After much deliberating, my rational mind overturned my initial decision and I left the hospital without being seen. "Where have you been?", my mum asked as I returned home at 6am. She had been at the window waiting in angst as she always did when I went on a night out. "Oh you know, just the casino then back to a mate's for a couple of drinks," I replied as I darted up the stairs and into my room. Some things are better left unsaid...

Cognitive Behavioural Therapy

My appointment with the psychologist was a disappointment. This was possibly because of my lack of commitment and scepticism about cognitive behavioural therapy. At the start of the session, we discussed my anxiety and the impact it was having on my life. We talked about the dreaded Rosemount and my need to avoid certain areas that made me feel uncomfortable. The psychologist made a parallel between my anxiety about locations with someone who had a phobia of spiders. She explained an approach to therapy that would include repeated exposure to Rosemount, in the hope of minimising or possibly even eliminating my phobia.

While I could see the relevance of this, I did not feel that it would work for me, nor was I sure if I wanted it to. I had been in Rosemount several times and could not envisage a time in the future where I would ever feel comfortable in that location. Besides, why would I want to go somewhere that made me feel anxious and uncomfortable? Even if this method could be successful in combating my fear of Rosemount, this was just one of many anxiety-inciting areas. It would take a lifetime to desensitise myself to them all, not to mention the need I felt for me to address other issues.

My reluctance to co-operate was evident from the outset. I could not help showing little enthusiasm for her suggested techniques. Note that I am not, in any way, trying to criticise CBT: I can appreciate how important it is in helping some people to overcome their difficulties. However, for me personally, I believe that a more beneficial course of action would have involved an in-depth analysis of the workings of my mind, and how that related to my behaviour. Had I been more open to change, perhaps this approach could have worked, especially if it had been used in conjunction with psychotherapy. However, I do not like change. No, it's stronger than that. I am completely averse to change, especially when it impinges on who I am and how I function. So it is not surprising that any attempt to try and change my thought processes, was by all accounts, hopeless. I am also a firm believer that you have to really want something in order to change. In fact, when I want something, I go the extra mile to get it. Even when my approach is not working, I will keep trying until I succeed or find something to replace it.

Anyway, I think I have made my point – CBT was not for me.

The Court Case

I was 19 years old, jobless, without a degree and I had failed miserably in my attempt to win back Steve. I was sitting at home contemplating my life one day when I received a surprising text from Colin (Steve's friend), asking if I wanted to go over to Steve's flat for some ahem… three-way action. I was not attracted to Colin, but this was hardly justification for saying no. The benefit of spending time with my lifelong obsession (which may sound a bit dramatic but it certainly felt this way) outweighed the negatives of having to be intimate with someone I did not fancy: so it was a decision that required minimal deliberation. Incidentally, the fact that Steve was still in a relationship with Emily - the girl he was with the night I saw him in the pub – held no bearing on my decision. Steve and Colin picked me up from my parent's house and took me to the flat for the inevitable. To say it was awkward is a bit of an understatement. I was still a virgin and had never done anything more than kissing. Even that was a rarity that had only happened on nights out with someone I hardly knew. It had always felt forced and slightly unnatural, far from the experience of two people in love, connecting through intimate acts.

In my mind, kissing is just something you do when you fancy someone, and the feeling is reciprocated. It is also something you might do when you are really drunk and you don't have the heart to say "no" when someone has been buying you drinks all night.

Steve and Colin seemed so confident as they ushered me through to Steve's bedroom and took off their clothes. I couldn't help but wonder if it was something they had done before. I lay down on Steve's bed, fully clothed and sandwiched in between both men. I felt incredibly awkward and uncomfortable, unable to focus on anything other than how to protect myself from Colin: preferably by removing him from the equation. A part of me felt obliged to follow through with the arrangement but in that moment, my body and mind would not allow for physical intimacy with anyone other than Steve. I just couldn't go there with Colin. It was wrong on so many levels. Somehow, I managed to get rid of Colin and was left with Steve. We did 'get together'.

It was…you know, so… so. Not that I had anything to compare it with. In truth, I was probably a bit bored but that seemed irrelevant. It was never about the sex. The sex was simply a means to an end, the method by which I would woo Steve and make him want me. *He will still want to be with me after having sex, right? Oh but wait, do I really want to be with him if he is no longer a challenge? I cannot believe I just had sex with Steve, with anyone. This is a huge development.* With my Steve neural network fully activated, I had much to analyse and mentally re-enact before our next encounter.

I was jobless, skint and desperate for work, but I had exhausted my options in the centre. The club where Steve worked seemed like a plausible option as they were always looking for bartenders, but I was wary. I did not want Steve to think that I was stalking him, so I had to think a bit outside the box. *How can I earn money and feel comfortable at the same time? Ah hah, The Horse and Dove pub, the club's sister company.* It was a small, intimate place with a mixed clientele, both young and old and definitely not pretentious. The pub was close to the police station, making it a convenient place for officers to congregate after their shift. Okay, so far so good. It was definitely somewhere I could see myself working. I was not particularly familiar with the location, so it did not evoke negative emotions when I went in to apply for the job, with my mum in tow for moral support. My mum used her charm and played the "not too obvious" desperation card to get me the job: "Francesca suffers from anxiety but she is such a nice girl. Please give her a chance to prove herself. She won't let you down".

The people seemed friendly and it was a buzzing environment to work in, with decent music adding to the vibe. I am not exactly a food and drink connoisseur, but I knew how to work a till and I could competently fill and empty a dishwasher. The rest of it would come over time…or so I thought. I made silly mistakes to begin with: whiskey in wine glasses, red wine in the fridge, beer with three heads – this was mostly down to my lack of knowledge and experience, some of which improved over time. I remember a time when there was a function held at the back bar of the pub and I was the designated bartender for the evening. It was okay to begin with since I was very much in control of the situation and everyone seemed satisfied with the service. However, as more and more people arrived and the drinks began to flow, I got stressed and started mixing up their orders. Then, as if by magic, I somehow managed to lose their entire tab. *Oh shit, how do I get myself out of this one?*

The shift manager was one of those arrogant, self-centred people who thought he was superior to everyone else. I was not prepared to admit my defeat to someone who terrified me into sub-mission. In desperation, I made up a new tab and entered a bunch of random drinks until the running total appeared to be reasonable, albeit slightly underestimated to avoid overcharging and receiving complaints. Remarkably, the imaginary tab was accepted as it was and my mistake went unnoticed – by the manager that is. I am sure the customer identified the unusual collection of drinks on their bill but for such a good price, how could they complain. I am sure the stock levels would have aroused suspicion but fortunately, I was not around long enough to find out.

I have a lot of admiration for waitresses. The art of juggling conversation with serving food and keeping track of multiple orders all at the same time is a mystery to me. Multi-tasking has never been my strong point. I could just about manage table service for one, but add another person or, God forbid, another table competing for service, and I was incapable of doing my job efficiently. I guess my approach to table service was a bit random; on one occasion, I even managed to take someone's order with my handbag on my arm – seriously, who does that? Common sense and logic would tell you to remove your handbag before you start work. Moreover, it was a great big heavy bag containing my purse, make-up and an array of nonsensical items I had accumulated over time. I only noticed when the strap slipped from my shoulder as I was attempting to write down the order, offering my customer a snapshot of the type of service they would receive while dining with Fran.

During one particular shift, I was on my lunch break and enjoying some pub grub (the food there was amazing) when I received a text from guess who? He asked what I was up to and if I wanted to go to his for dessert – not literally but metaphorically speaking, meaning he wanted to have sex. I was semi-excited to hear from him again. The anxiety that always accompanied me while I was at work made it extremely difficult to feel what I should have felt under such circumstances: pure joy and elation. I sent a short, direct reply and, through a series of short texts, we arranged to meet the following night.

I went to his flat the following evening for our second sexual encounter. It was just the two of us this time. The sex was nothing to write home about – pretty basic by any standards – but he wanted me and that was all that mattered. *Well… he didn't explicitly say that he wanted me but of course he did… why wouldn't he? He wouldn't have asked to have sex again if he didn't want to be with me?* The repeat performance signified a new development in our relationship. What it had developed into, I did not know, but I felt that each encounter was sure to strengthen the bond between us.

I do not recall feeling any emotion during our intimate time together. It was certainly not one of those "I am so in love with you" moments. It was more a case of in out, in out, shake it all about and cum (on his part, not mine). I was performing an act, or at least letting him perform an act on me (my input was minimal).

Thinking about it now, I guess I felt used and dirty afterwards – as if I had carried out a wrongful act. Actually, this isn't far from the truth… I had slept with someone who was in a relationship with someone else. This was not only morally wrong but it also demonstrated a lack of consideration towards his girlfriend and a lack of self-respect. I don't even think I fancied him physically: I mean, I did not find him attractive per se, but he did make me feel good about myself. And, in any case, he was a prize that I was determined to win.

God, that sounds awful… it is awful. Many would argue (including myself in retrospect) that I deserved to be punished for my inappropriate behaviour. If it hadn't been for me being so obsessed with wooing Steve, I would never have contemplated sex with someone who was unavailable. However, I do develop obsessions that influence my behaviour, and I would be lying if I tried to sugar coat this in any other way.

What I know and how I behave are often two disparate things. This is especially true when I am driven more by my emotions than by logic and my moral compass (which is admittedly slightly skewed).

It was because of my emotional drive, that I had no qualms about becoming friends with Steve's girlfriend. This friendship stemmed from a message Emily sent to me in response to a message from me she had found on Steve's phone. *"You are a slut, who walks like a man and has small boobs".*

The first and the latter were definitely not true but perhaps I did walk a little like a man (and still do). In any case, I had no justification for my behaviour and, given that she had every right to be angry, I had no reason to retaliate in anger. From there on in, we developed a sort of online friendship where we would text each other from time to time, just general chit chat about music and life, learning about each other's interests (outside of Steve).

Why did we become friends? There's a simple answer. She was insecure (and had every reason to be) and for me, she was another link to my obsession. We texted on and off for a while until I became a little too obsessed and the conversation had become one-sided – between me and myself. I think she tired of me (either that or I was no longer a threat) and her messages began to wane. I was of course disappointed, but as she was not the absolute focus of my attention, I could just about cope with the rejection. She was, after all, just one of the many connections I had to Steve, albeit a major one.

I have often overhead people saying that they have learned from their mistakes and, having tried and failed, they would never go down the same path twice. I, on the other hand, tend to persist in the behaviour I am using to try and reach a goal, despite it clearly not working. This could be a relationship, work project or anything else I am trying to achieve. In fact, failure motivates me and makes me more determined to succeed, thus strengthening the neural network for my goal-driven behaviour. While my dedication and persistence are something to be commended, my inability to learn from my mistakes results in the same negative outcomes, time and time again.

My experience with Steve is one example of this. Unfortunately, while it was the first time I engaged in an unhealthy and illicit relationship, it was not the last. By contrast, when I engage in the right type of behaviour, I reap the rewards… but I'll say more about this later.

The night after my second sexual experience with Steve, I went out clubbing, on a high and determined to dance the night away. I was so excited to see Steve under new and advanced circumstances. Internal dialogue and rhetorical Steve questions were bombarding my mind as I prepared for the big night…*will he be equally excited to see me? Of course he will be. Perhaps he will be a little coy at first, trying not to glance in my direction to avoid making his desires too obvious. There is no denying the fact he wants to be with me. I cannot wait to see the expression on his face when I enter the club.* This all seemed too good to be true… was it? Should I have been preparing myself for a fall?

The drinks were flowing nicely and I was on good form, feeling like a celebrity who was about to go on stage to be admired from afar. Thankfully, Sarah was also on top form – we were good at bringing each other up or down to the desired level of optimism, depending on the other's mood. After a great night of drinking, laughing, flirting and dancing, it was time for the club to close and I plucked up the courage to approach Steve. He was standing on the stairs watching the drunks from above, in anticipation of a fight breaking out. "Hi, how are you?" (I didn't usually speak to him: I just observed him observing me). Silence. He was clearly ignoring me.

"What is wrong?" I asked.

He told me I knew what the problem was and instructed me to leave. I was so confused, hurt and rejected. He told me his girlfriend knew everything and it was over. *No, it can't be. You cannot sleep with me then dismiss me like this.*

I begged him to talk to me but he continued to ignore me. I was trying to hold back the tears and hide the emotional pain that was consuming me. Sarah had left early to meet her boyfriend and

I had ended up with an old school friend, Jennifer, who was trying to usher me out of the club. Reluctantly, I waited outside for Steve. A couple of the other bouncers appeared but there was no sign of him. I asked them where he was and they told me that he had left through the back door. So not only had I been rejected, but he was now avoiding me. I was crushed.

Right that is it! I was on a mission. *There is absolutely no way I am going to let this go.* I immediately hailed a taxi, and got into the front passenger seat with tears streaming down my face, while Jennifer hopped in the back seat. Through my tears, I directed the taxi driver to the village where Steve lived. I had no idea what I was going to do when I got there, but I was determined to confront him, and nothing or no one was going to get in my way.

The entrance to his property was on the rear side of the building, away from prying eyes. Jennifer and I, still intoxicated, staggered up some steps to the front door of his flat. Ring, bang, bang… and repeat. No answer. There were a couple of items sitting outside the front door, including an umbrella and a pair of boots that were strategically placed on the top step. It didn't take long before frustration kicked in and the items went flying down the stairs and into the garden below. *Why is he not answering? Is he scared of me? He should be.*

I was looking for a reaction and as I wasn't getting one, I had to find an alternative way to capture his attention. I threw a small stone at the window, which prompted Jennifer to propose an alternative, more extreme method of provoking a reaction. "If you are going to do it properly, do it with a brick". I wasn't sure if she was being serious or not, but I took her suggestion literally. I descended the steps and into the garden, where, conveniently enough, I found a small collection of bricks in the corner of the garden, next to a shed. I picked up one of the bricks and climbed back up the stairs, ready to make my presence known in a more assertive, destructive way. Without hesitation, I lobbed the brick through the kitchen window. Smash, crash, clatter. He must have left some cutlery on the side-board as the sound of plates smashing emanated from the scene.

"I can't believe you did that," Jennifer shouted. Neither could I. It was time to leave. We scurried off, put some distance between ourselves and the house, then called for a taxi to take us home.

When I woke up the following morning, I had a sinking feeling in the pit of my stomach. What had I done? My phone, that was perched on the side table, was flashing – indicating message received. Tentatively, I picked up my phone and opened the inbox. "You have a new message from Steve". Waves of shame and embarrassment flooded through my mind. I was shaking, partly with nervous anticipation and also because I had the shakes after a night of heavy drinking. The message read: "that wasn't very nice, was it?" Apparently, one of the bouncers had warned him about my behaviour and he, quite wisely, had watched me in action from afar – inside his car.

I was completely distraught and unable to hide it from my parents, even if I wanted to. Their disappointment was overridden by worry and concern – not only for my mental health, but also about the possibility of legal action being taken against me. But I was not in the right frame of mind to care about that. My main priority was to regain control and restore my personal well-being.

Sure enough, the police arrived at my door later that evening. My mum called me down from my room before she invited the two policemen in to discuss the inevitable. "We have been called in relation to an incident on Gordon Road on Friday the 20th August 2009, at 4.00am: Francesca Baird has been accused of throwing a brick through the kitchen window of this property, which is also the accuser's home". I was impressed at the policeman's ability to say this with a straight face… I am not sure what a criminal looks like, but I am sure if you were to conjure up an image, it would be nothing like me.

After confirming that I was indeed Francesca Baird and obtaining my admission of guilt, they informed me that Steve was taking legal action in response to the damage caused. They also advised me to keep my distance from him and his property. My mum couldn't resist the temptation to intervene… "You boys are attractive in that uniform… I bet you would like to date one of them, Francesca? I know you are just doing your job, but you must know that Francesca is a good person. She is usually well behaved but this boy really hurt her. To be honest, he probably deserved it. You have met him right? What did you think of him? He is not worth it, is he?" The flattery and excuses for my behaviour did not make an ounce of difference to the outcome, but the policemen did warm to us. They couldn't resist the temptation to remove their hardened exterior and engage in a little bit of banter. As they were leaving, one of them told my mum, "I can tell she is a nice girl but she does not need us to tell her that you cannot go around throwing bricks through people's windows. I am afraid it is out of our hands". I hadn't had a chance to answer at that time, but yes, of course I fancied them. They were aloof, attractive, in a position of authority (a step above Steve) and dressed to impress. What was there not to like?

A few days had passed since the brick incident. This hadn't been enough time to let the dust settle and get back in the game. I had made things extremely difficult for myself and I had to consider the possibility that Steve would never speak to me again. However, if he understood how I felt and that my behaviour had been reactive – a response to the internal pain he had inflicted on me – then maybe, over time, he would forgive me. I decided that a night out was the best solution to my current dilemma, as it would also provide me with the chance to confront Steve face to face. If I could explain why I threw the brick, then he might downgrade his current perception of me from "complete psychopath who needs to be locked up" to "vulnerable girl, with issues, crying out for support"… or perhaps, on reflection, he would consider his actions and see he had been wrong: maybe he would even apologise for the part he played in my Jekyll to Hyde transformation that night. After a brief, empowering conversation with Sarah, my feelings changed from pessimism and depression to optimism and sheer determination to "get back in control". This was something we both said frequently, at times when we had behaved "out of character" and needed to reconstruct our self-images.

I've mentioned this before, but I LOVE A CHALLENGE! In fact, the more unachievable the challenge is, the more rewarding it is if I succeed. I may have been facing an uphill battle, but I was determined. I was going to win Steve back, but first I had to make him like me again – so, Operation Win Back Steve, here we come.

The preamble to the big night out involved the consumption of alcoholic drinks in rapid succession with Sarah and Alana while we shared encouraging words of wisdom, which became exponentially more uplifting and positively reinforcing with each drink consumed. This was our not so clever attempt to restore some confidence before my next social encounter with Steve.

The night was progressing well, and I was feeling good as we approached the club… although I was also a bit desperate in my need to speak to Steve and get it all out of my system. In good form and with my head held high, I walked in between the bouncers and into the club. I was surprised when the bouncer tapped me on the shoulder and said, "Not tonight love". Oh shit, I immediately felt anxious, verging on panic stricken – *well how long am I banned for?*

*Life. Oh ok…. now wait a minute – did he just say… LIFE? Holy fuck! So let me get this straight. I am banned for life, from the club I attend six nights a week, and one of the only places where Steve could admire me from afar, and all because I threw a brick through his bloody window. This is ludicrous…*I soon came to realise that there was no way I was getting past the bouncers. I had no option but to accept my defeat. I cried all the way home and for the next few days.

To say I never make life easy for myself is a wild understatement. One of my most annoying and unchangeable traits is my inability to regulate my emotions and my desire to feel deep and intense emotions – good or bad. Of course, positive emotions are slightly preferable to negative ones… but in the absence of pure elation, I would prefer to feel pain than nothing at all.

That may seem a strong statement: but it is also true. I cannot say for sure, but I don't believe I understand the subtle emotions many people encounter daily, nor do I know if I want to feel less intense emotions. Having said this, it is exhausting being me. My anxiety-riddled brain does not help my cause either, as it craves something to worry about all the time: this is my survival strategy in this unpredictable world.

I have said it before and I will say it again: "normal life" terrifies me. By creating my fantasies and putting myself in impossibly difficult situations, I can escape real life and the challenges that accompany it. It's the only way I know how to be and is integral to my sense of self. Therefore, any attempt to change my way of thinking and regulate my emotions has been short lived. However, I can at least safely say that my brick throwing days are well behind me.

Correction, I think those days are behind me… but as I am sure you are aware, my behaviour to date suggests that I do not learn from my mistakes as history has a habit of repeating itself in my life. In hindsight, I do wonder if the brick incident was, on some level, predetermined by my unconscious. If it hadn't been for the brick, perhaps I would have found another means of escaping Steve and my internal suffering. As I did not have the strength to consciously walk away, I wonder if I deliberately put myself in an uncompromising situation, so that difficult decisions would be taken out of my hands: in other words I would be banned from seeing Steve. After that, I did not have the option of seeing Steve. It would be impossible to continue my infatuation when I could not see him, so it ultimately saved me from further heartache.

Of course, that did not stop my conscious mind from making one last ditch attempt to find my way back into his life, as at the time I saw the ban as just another obstacle to be overcome in my pursuit of him.

So, I had been banned from the club where Steve worked, for LIFE. However, at the time, I was still working for the club's sister company. Fortunately, I had become friendly with one of the managers who knew about my situation and was supportive, ensuring that I did not lose my job.

I did, however, find it difficult when the staff went clubbing after work. I had the choice of going out on my own or going home and retire to my bed. Actually – that is not strictly true. My friend and work colleague Fiona had a plan, one that would keep the group together without deviating from the normal routine. A perk of working for the club's sister company included discounted drinks there, making it almost impossible for me to persuade my colleagues to try another club. My motives were somewhat different from theirs but ultimately, we wanted the same thing: to go to my favourite club. The plan was simple. I just had to get past the doormen without being seen.

Of course, i had been here before, when I was underage. But this time was different. Having progressed from my invisible status to being called "love" and "darling", to being on first name terms with the bouncers, I had become a regular. I knew it was a long shot trying to go back to being invisible, but after a few drinks to build my confidence and a bit of moral support from my colleagues, I was on board. This was one week on from my lifelong ban.

Miraculously, I managed to walk in between the bouncers without being challenged. I suppose it is possible they saw me and chose to turn a blind eye but it didn't really matter as I had achieved the first goal of the night – gaining entrance to the club. Goal number two was to remain in the club without being thrown out. This was completely out of my control but I was hoping that Steve would forgive and forget. The girls headed straight up to the bum pinching floor for a good boogie (I really must stop saying that word). Sheepishly, I followed. We took the stairs nearest the entrance to avoid Steve, who was stationed on the first floor. I think he spotted me but as I was trying not to look, I could not be sure. As we reached our destination a sense of relief came over me. That was until I overheard one of the bouncers (a new guy I did not know although he obviously knew me) putting his counter terrorism skills into practice as he not so discreetly shared my whereabouts over the radio: "She is on the third floor, wearing a black top and grey jeans and is currently making her way towards the bar. Roger that". It could only have been me they were talking about. I was certain of this, as the bouncer was looking right at me. *Oh shit. What do I do now?* After a quick game of hide and seek, they (plural) caught up with me and escorted me out of the club. I am not one for causing a scene, not really anyway, and I did not want to appear like a stalker, so I duly did as I was told and left the club.

A few weeks after the brick incident, I was chilling at home, minding my own business, when my mum handed me an envelope. The content was self-evident from the police logo on the top right-hand corner. I immediately opened it and skimmed through the waffle to the part where I was invited to attend court. While I understood that my actions had consequences, I could not help but feel an overriding sense of anger towards Steve. *How did it come to this? I am not a criminal. Am I?*

I felt that Steve should have understood and tried to resolve the issue without taking such extreme action. Should I really have been held accountable for my behaviour or could it have been justified as a rational response to being mistreated by my man? There were mitigating circumstances. I had been provoked... *but was I? Oh shit, how could I have been so stupid? There must be something I can do to rectify this situation and redeem myself.*

After much deliberation and to-ing and fro-ing, I mustered up the courage to text Steve to ask for forgiveness, hoping it might even evoke sympathy in him. I cannot remember exactly what the message said but I suspect it was something along the lines of, "I apologise for my behaviour but you must understand that I was overcome with emotion (not to mention intoxicated). Not only am I regretful for my behaviour but I have been asked to attend court over this matter. This is serious".

I was trying to feel optimistic, but given his rate of response to previous messages, I did not really expect a reply. So I was pleasantly surprised when the screen on my phone lit up and his name appeared next to an envelope symbol. The message read, "pay for the window and I will drop the charges".

To be honest, my feelings of elation at receiving a message from Steve outweighed the sense of relief a person feels when excused from their legal obligations. Correct me if I am wrong, but I saw this as a good sign as it demonstrated a level of forgiveness on his part and suggested he had softened to me.

I immediately agreed to pay for the window in the hope that this would somehow alleviate his negative feelings towards me – and, of course, being excused from court would be a bonus. I transferred £750 into his account the following day and attended court a couple of weeks later. Apparently, he had asked for the charges to be dropped but by then it was too late. My fate would now be decided by a greater power, one that neither of us had any control over.

Sarah and I wore our best suits for the big day. My hearing was late in the afternoon, giving us plenty of time to have lunch in the centre and walk past Steve, looking like professional business-women on a mission. I did not know what to expect as we entered the courtroom. I certainly hadn't envisaged a room full of people, waiting to be reprimanded for minor offences. I was half expecting jurors to appear but thankfully, the jury box was empty, and the only official was a rather intimidating female judge, with a stern look and hardened exterior, fulfilling her role to a tee.

Sarah and I stuck out like a sore thumb in our suits. We obviously hadn't received the memo about the dress code – joggers and a hoody – as we were the only people in the room, apart from the lawyers and judge, who were dressed up for the occasion. We sat and watched as a couple of youths were prosecuted for theft. Interestingly, all of the suspects seemed to have lawyers representing them and thus were excused from speaking. I took a seat in one of the front benches, far from prying eyes, and I pondered...perhaps I should have considered my options before rocking on up to court without any preconceived ideas or expectations as to how the day would unfold.

When it was finally my turn to be heard, I was asked if I had someone representing me. I informed them that I was representing myself and I was called up to stand in the witness box, just like it happens on TV. As the judge read out the offence, I overheard people at the back of the room sniggering and talking among themselves. To be fair, I probably would have done the same thing if I was an observer, but I was too busy trying to process the surreal experience to care about what anyone else was thinking. "How do you plead?" the judge finally asked when she had finished going over the details of the crime. I did not try to defend or justify my behaviour with my response: "I plead guilty. I was acting on my emotions and I am extremely regretful for my actions. I am aware that there is no excuse for my behaviour, and I have since paid for the damage". After a couple of minutes' deliberation, the verdict was reached… my case was admonished (meaning I would receive the lightest sentence possible under Scottish law, although I would still have a criminal record).

It could have been worse I thought, as the judge issued a stern warning and declared that I was free to go.

Moving On

In the following weeks, I was short of money and there was an increasing pressure to consider my options, in terms of work and the possibility of developing a career. Due to his pure inaccessibility, my optimism about winning Steve back was beginning to wane. I was however, determined to take back control and do something with my life. I had no choice really. It was either that or succumb to depression, and I was beginning to tire of my struggles.

My desire to be in a position of power, combined with my childhood dream of joining the police made the decision-making process relatively easy. I had been hesitant about applying up until this point, since attending road accidents and visiting hospitals didn't seem well suited to a hypochondriac. I had also been concerned about my suitability for the job due to my need for routine and the logistical complications that would arise from the inevitability of having to enter anxiety-provoking locations. Picture the scene, there I am behind the wheel of the police car, driving at full speed during a police chase while engaged in running commentary over the radio when… oh shit… the suspect is heading west on North Mount Street towards Rosemount… mission aborted!

My fear of death had somehow dissipated over the years – or at least it had been replaced by my obsession with Steve. But I still had anxiety about potential disruptions to my routine. Nevertheless, I had nothing to lose by applying, so I completed the application and submitted it before I had time to change my mind.

I was surprised and terrified when I received a letter a couple of weeks later, inviting me to attend the initial assessment in the recruitment process. Panic immediately consumed me as I began to process the possibility of actually becoming a police officer. I was desperately trying to imagine my future as a member of the force and, in doing so, asked myself the following rhetorical questions: *where would I be stationed? Would I fit in or feel isolated? What would my shift patterns be like? What if I had to work night shifts? I am always more anxious at night. How would I cope with the disruption to my sleep patterns? Could I handle the pressures of the job? What if I had to attend a serious accident and someone died? The mental imagery of the scene would stay with me, affecting every aspect of my life from there on in. Do I have any control over any of this? This job could be an opportunity but could also lead to my demise.*

There were so many unknowns and my brain was struggling to construct an accurate representation of how my life would unfold as a member of the police force: I didn't know whether it would be the making of me or would be detrimental to my health. I consciously stopped my thoughts in their tracks, as I reminded myself that I still had a long way to go in the recruitment process and that I was not committed to anything, yet.

Beforehand, I'd say there was only a 50/50 chance of me even turning up to the assessment. However, my parents drove me to the assessment centre and, after waiting outside for five minutes, were pleasantly surprised when I did not return to the car. I guess I was feeling positive that day as I somehow managed, after encouraging words from my parents, to push the boundaries and seize the opportunity I had been presented with.

The exam comprised a short series of questions, testing my English and maths ability. The questions were relatively easy and I was reasonably confident that I had passed. It was a good month or so before I heard anything, and I was overjoyed when I received a letter stating that I had passed my exam and I was through to the next stage of the recruitment process.

I was still unsure how I would cope if I were to successfully get through the entire recruitment process, but passing my exam was a confidence booster if nothing else. Not only was it evidence of my ability to overcome my anxieties and attend the initial assessment, but it showed that I had a sufficiently functioning brain, at least to the extent that it had enabled me to answer enough questions correctly.

Unfortunately, my "can do" attitude was short lived. A couple of weeks later, I received a disappointing letter from the police, retracting their initial decision: "I am afraid you have been unsuccessful on this occasion and we will not be taking you any further in the process. It is the Chief Constable's right not to give you a reason why".

It didn't take much analysis before I reached the obvious conclusion: they do not recruit brick throwers to the police. As my mum always said, "what is for you in life won't go by you". This is possibly a load of mumbo jumbo, but it was a comforting thought at the time, to believe that a career in the police was simply not for me. I consciously made the decision to stay well clear of anything police-related for a while as I pulled myself together and reconsidered my future options.

Desperate to move on from Steve, I went on multiple dates in short succession. The internet site I used was not popular at the time and deemed by most as uncool, but I didn't care. I was looking to meet someone with interests other than going out, getting drunk and pulling random girls. The dating site seemed the best option, possibly the only option, given my lack of hobbies and disinterest in joining social clubs of any kind.

I knew it would take someone special to allow me to move on from Steve and my expectations were low until… there he was, my match, the one I was destined to be with. He was average looking, with a warm manly face, and short, dark, unstyled hair. In fact, facially, he reminded me of one of my teenage crushes, Gary Barlow. I scrolled down to see more photos, but he only had the headshot that he was using as his profile picture. This pleased me; any more photos might have made him seem a poser – unless of course it was a photo of him participating in a sport or engaged in one his hobbies – this is the only exception to the rule.

From the brief correspondence we had using the site's messaging service, my impression was of someone sensible, grounded, and open minded. More importantly, he did not put kisses or emojis at the end of his messages. I know it sounds silly, possibly even pedantic but I cannot understand why people finish a message with emojis, especially when they do not know the other person. It is perhaps okay if you are in a romantic relationship or in love, but even then, I think it would make me cringe. I once dated a guy who finished every message with multiple kisses and hug emojis! Unsurprisingly, our relationship was short and sweet.

I met the Gary Barlow look-alike at a pub in town. The date was in the afternoon and I was driving, to avoid making a drunken fool of myself in front of my future husband. I was genuinely excited about meeting him, which was strange given that up until that point Steve had been the only person to have that effect on me.

I had mentioned my pending date to my parents and told them I thought he would be the one and that I had a good feeling about him. He sent me a message just before I arrived to let me know that he was standing at the bar, not that I would have missed him since there was no one else in the bar. As I approached him and he turned around, I was stunned by the contrast between the man I had envisaged and the boy standing before me. He looked much younger in real life and had a great big cheesy grin plastered across his face: he looked very different to how he had looked in the photo. His face was… well red, bright red, like a beacon of redness acting as a focal

103

point in the dark club. It is no exaggeration to say that he had the reddest face I have ever seen in my life. Unfortunately, I was not attracted to him – not just because of the red face, but because he just didn't meet my expectations in any way – and although the conversation flowed well, I am sure he could sense the disappointment in me. He seemed like a nice, interesting person, but I had already made up my mind, there was no chemistry between us. He did send me a message the following day, asking to meet again. I tried my best to let him down gently and that was the end of that.

The more dates I went on, the lower my expectations became. I went on a cinema date with a boy named Chris, who I had met on a more popular dating website. At the time, internet dates were beginning to gain popularity among singletons, thereby increasing my options and making it statistically more likely that I would meet the man of my dreams. Chris picked me up from my parents' house in his super-duper fancy, great big Land Rover. My nosey mother, who was conveniently in the kitchen at the time and just so happened to be looking out of the window, shouted, "Oh my God, he has a fancy car and looks like someone out of *Baywatch*".

I was excited as I shut the front door and headed towards the car, while ensuring that my head stayed firmly fixed on whatever was in front of me to avoid unnecessary eye contact with my date. I also refrained from looking up at the window so I did not have to acknowledge the gestures my mother would be making to embarrass me. As I got into the passenger seat beside him, I could not help but notice his strong arms – one partially out of the window, with the elbow resting on the driver side door. His other arm was firmly stuck to the gears, smoothly shifting them from time to time with an air of being cool, calm and collected.

I couldn't help but notice the rather expensive looking watch on his left wrist. I could not determine the make but I suspect it was

Rolex or *Breitling* or something similar. First impressions were good, at least up until the moment we both stepped/fell out of his beast of a vehicle. I looked over the bonnet of his car but Chris was nowhere to be seen. Until, oh there he was… I spotted him as he walked out in front of the car, sporting an unnecessary swagger. OMG! He was so small that I could not even see him over the bonnet of his car. At the risk of sounding shallow, height is not a major deal breaker for me when it comes to dating but, as a rule of thumb, I am unwilling to date someone who is smaller than me. Given that I am small and petite, finding someone taller than me has never been an issue, up until this date, that is. The poor guy never stood a chance.

I have also dated men who were either after only one thing or who developed intense romantic feelings from the offset. For example, one guy started crying when I ended it. He said that he was in love with me and just wanted to be loved back, despite the fact we were only on our third date. Another man tried to kiss me on our second date, during a walk in one of my comfort zones. I refused and told him it was too soon… why on earth would I kiss someone I did not know, especially when I was sober? When we had finished the walk, just before we parted ways, he tried to kiss me again. As I pulled away, he said "Oh, too soon?"

Another date is worth mentioning, not because of the date itself but because of my mum's not so discreet spying tactics. I made the big mistake of telling my mum where we would be meeting on our first date: I really should have known better. We were sitting in *Starbucks* when I spotted my mum hiding behind a pillar in the shopping centre. She kept peering out, meerkat-style, from behind the pillar, then retreating into her original hiding position. A couple of teenage girls sitting beside me were staring and laughing at the strange woman hiding behind a pillar. Fortunately, my date was sitting opposite me and had not initially noticed. By contrast, with my restless mannerisms and wandering eye, I was distracted by my mother's presence and it didn't take long before curiosity got the better of him and he turned around to see what I was looking at. He did of course, instantly spot her and, just as he was about to ask if I knew who she was, I intervened with: "The crazy woman behind the pillar is my mum and she is spying on us, sorry". Fortunately, he just laughed and waved.

She also did a similar thing with my most recent, short-term boyfriend. We were on our third or fourth date and had decided to take my dog for a run around the grassy area opposite my parents' house. My mum, not so subtly, hid behind a bush and watched. He noticed her before I did (the wonders of Facebook): "Er, I think that is your mum hiding behind that bush". Of course, it was, I didn't need to look to know it was her. We both just laughed and carried on, secretly observing her observing us, oblivious to the fact we had spotted her in action.

While reflecting on these incidents, I have come to realise that part of my problem is my desire for my mum's approval – in every aspect of my life, from what to wear on a night out to whom I should date – my mum has always been at the core of the family, controlling the thoughts and functions of her offspring. There is a metaphor my mum uses that succinctly describes this aspect of our relationship; she refers to me as a little bird, attached to a string although every so often I attempt to fly out of my nest and venture into the unknown. Each day she will let me go a little bit further but will always pull me back in to the nest, where I am safe and protected from the big bad world.

Bear in mind I was in my 20s when she came up with this fairly accurate metaphor. As a result of my mum's attitude, my siblings and I are all extremely close to her. My sisters share every little detail of their lives with her, and rely on her approval before making decisions. In fact, my sister even called my mum to tell her that her new boyfriend had just tasted his first pork pie.

Sex is also discussed openly within the family. My mum often asks us about our sex lives, both past and present. My eldest sister freely divulges such information, but I am a little more guarded in my responses. There are some things you do not want to discuss with your mum, and for me, sex is one of them. Having said that, if you share a secret with one member of the family, then the entire family (including extended family) will know by the end of the day, without exception. Just like Chinese Whispers, the story goes full circle and back to the originator sounding more dramatic and skewed from the truth.

Then there is the fall out with respect to the lack of privacy within the family, and so on. Moral of the story: do not share private information with family members unless you want the whole world to know. Trust me, there are no revelations that will surprise my family in this book, which is just as well really.

Anyway, where was I… ah yes… my mum was desperate for me to have a boyfriend and was concerned that I would never connect with anyone. She was accustomed to my dating routine: a single date only – which was commonplace – means that the initial attraction is not there. Two or three dates means that there is something about the person I like but I need to spend a bit more time with them before I conclude that I cannot see it progressing. Four plus dates means there is potential – often this means that the person is attractive, and we get along well. It is usually at this point I allow my mum to meet them (if she hasn't "inadvertently" met them already) and, more often than not, demonstrate her approval. Common phrases she uses include "You are so handsome. I know people and I can tell that you are a lovely boy. Stick with Francesca as she needs someone like you, and I could be doing with a son in law like you.

How old are you? If Francesca is not interested, then I definitely am".

The relationship may or may not progress past this stage. Indeed, it is quite common for me to date someone for two or three months with the hope of developing feelings over time. Unfortunately, my feelings do not grow with the passage of time, and I have no option but to set them free, with friendship being the most I can offer. Some men hang on in the hope that I will feel differently over time but, after a while, they realise that I cannot commit. In order to protect themselves from being hurt, they have no option but to terminate our friendship. Frustratingly for me, I have no qualms about letting them go and my only feeling is sorrow, both for myself and for my inability to connect on a deeper level, despite wanting to.

Pure O

After a while, I started a new job as a sales assistant in a clothing store, *Mantra*, located in my favourite centre. My fellow employees were mostly of a similar age, with a few motherly figures thrown into the mix for diversity, making me feel instantly at home. To estimate how long I was likely to want to stay working in the store, I spent a considerable amount of time analysing my new environment. The shop was bright and spacious, on two levels, with access from both the lower ground and upper floor of the centre. It was in the heart of the centre, creating a false perception of protection and comfort that I would not have felt on the peripheries. Moreover, the tills were positioned at the back of the shop, away from the entrances, adding to my feelings of safety and comfort in my immediate environment, and giving me less concern about the wider surroundings: the centre. This was a positive step on my journey to self-development as I discovered that I could experience feelings of comfort and security in isolation from Steve. For the first time since Steve had entered my life, I believed that I could move on and find something or someone else to fill that void. It was a brief and momentary thought but it was significant, since I had opened the door (metaphorically speaking) to the possibility of – dare I say it – change.

Conveniently, I developed good relationships with my colleagues and the managers, who appreciated my work ethic: I can be hard working, capable, driven and adaptable to a role, making me a valuable addition to the team. My role mainly consisted of customer service, till work and repeatedly tidying up after customers (a type of work I was very much accustomed to). However, despite feeling comfortable in my new role and environment, it did not take long before feelings of frustration and a burning desire for more, and to be more, took hold of me. To give you an idea of what I mean, try to imagine this – you have just arranged a section of clothing, with a thumb space between each garment, all facing the same way and sorted in an orderly fashion with matching items presented side by side to encourage additional spending. Then, as you stand back to admire your masterpiece, the dreaded customer appears and within a couple of minutes, some of the clothes have fallen off their hangers, some have been removed and reinserted the wrong way round or in the wrong location and then the customer wanders off without buying anything, totally oblivious to the destruction they have left behind. I swear there is nothing more frustrating than this – well, perhaps this is an exaggeration, but surely you can see why I was striving for more.

A year or so later, I left my job at *Mantra* and went to work for another fashion store, still within the centre. This time I was employed as Head of Department. Sounds good eh? Well it wasn't really. It was just a glorified title for someone in charge of their own section of clothing – whoop-di-do. It was a much bigger store than I was used to, the ambience was poor, the lights were bright (too bright), and dance music was pumping throughout: all within a crowded, fast paced environment. I felt like my brain was going to explode. I was isolated and stuck in my own section of the shop without the interconnectedness and team spirit I had experienced when working with others. Moreover, there were so many team members, all working different shifts and at different times, that it was difficult to get to know anyone and develop sustainable friendships. I felt overwhelmed and confused, as my mind tried to make sense of and control my environment but failed miserably. It felt as though my mind was out of sync with the rest of the world, as it tried to grapple with my new surroundings. A few weeks into the job, I couldn't take any more, so I left.

I picked up another job almost instantly, in another clothing store right next door to the one I had just left. Only this time, I had moved up in the world with my new sophisticated title being Office Manager. It was basically a back of house job, dealing with the financial aspects of the business, which involved cashing up and balancing the books at the end of play. At the end of the day, just as the shop was about to close, I would consciously navigate my way around the shop floor, pushing a heavy metal unit (almost the same size as me), on tiny wheels designed to hold multiple cash trays that were removed from the tills (12 trays to be exact). It was extremely difficult to negotiate my way around the isles with this impossibly heavy unit without crashing into rails of clothing. It was not one of my finest moments when the unit hit an uneven part of the floor one day and the whole thing toppled over with a less than subtle crash. Thankfully, the money remained within the locked unit. However, the money from each cash tray was no longer assigned to its corresponding till as the coins jumped from one tray to another on impact. Inevitably, I had to stay late that evening to reconcile the books. I was embarrassed and stressed by the situation which led me to make yet another impulsive decision, to leave my job immediately without notice.

I was fortunate enough to be re-employed by *Mantra*. So back I went, tail between my legs in acceptance that I had got it wrong and the grass had not been greener. Only this time it was different. I had a new position as full-time member of staff and with added responsibility: mostly paperwork, cashing up and staff training. The job was far more fulfilling that it had been, which in turn contributed to my feelings of self-worth. Within a short time, I was adept in my new role and re-accustomed to the environment. Ironically, it was at this time that I began to feel uneasy again. My focus had switched from adjusting to my routine and proving myself in the workplace, to... well... nothing. It sounds silly, I know, but as I have mentioned already, I needed a stressor in my life, an obsession to take over my thoughts and to simultaneously offer a level of comfort and anxiety. Without that mental distraction, life becomes normal and this, as we well know, scares me. Once again, I was becoming increasingly frustrated and it did not take long before old habits crept in and I started taking time off.

My manager Jenna was aware of my difficulties – what I describe as a mental paralysis preventing me from getting out of bed in the morning. I was lucky because she was not only understanding and supportive, but she genuinely cared and wanted to help me. At times of weakness, when I felt vulnerable, frustrated and on the edge of a meltdown, Jenna somehow managed to console me. On many occasions, I was fine one minute, then crying inconsolably the next, for no known reason. On such occasions, Jenna was there, providing support at work then checking up on me in the evening to make sure I was okay. In turn, I was extremely grateful and demonstrated this by working to the best of my ability. On an optimistic day, I would often pull it out the bag by performing well and surpassing my employer's expectation. I was bloody brilliant at gently persuading (to put it politely) customers to open store cards and outperformed my colleagues, both locally and regionally, in terms of the number of store cards opened by one member of staff, consistently and over a period of time. To give you an idea, there were between 20 and 30 members of staff in the store, and in an average week, approximately 30% of the total number of store cards opened had been personally instigated by me.

Why did I perform so well at this task? I can honestly say it was less about ability and more a result of self-determination and my desire to please others: more specifically, Jenna. I suppose guilt and redemption were another factor in my desire to succeed, since I wanted to redeem myself for having taken time off and for relying so heavily on Jenna for moral support. I also thrived on the recognition I received: a combination of praise from the boss and a small bonus for each card opened – a win-win for the brains reward system.

On a bad day, I would find myself pacing the shop floor, feeling anxious and frustrated, and craving a release mechanism for the accumulation of emotions that were bubbling away beneath the surface of my conscious mind. On a couple of occasions, I excused myself from the shop floor and went to the works toilets to release my emotions in solitude, by self-harming. I guess I did this partly for attention since the scars were a way to expose my internal pain and demonstrate externally how I was feeling on the inside. I wanted someone to save me, from what I do not know... possibly myself? What I do know, however, is that I still did not have the internal tools to regulate my own emotions. I also did not have the resolve to find a way out of the chaos that was consuming me. But I knew I needed help and I was determined to get it, somehow.

I went back to see the doctor, in the hope of getting the right support this time. It was a new doctor who had been relocated to the practice, which meant we had to have a brief discussion about my history, including my anxiety, my obsessions and the repetitive thoughts that consumed me. She was sympathetic to my wants and needs and, without hesitation, referred me to see a clinical psychologist. I didn't have to wait long for the preliminary meeting and, after describing my symptoms for the umpteenth time, the psychologist was confident in her initial assessment. I had a form of OCD called Pure O – basically the obsessions without the compulsions. This made sense, but it didn't seem to explain all my problems, including my inability to regulate my emotions. Part of me was grateful for the professional analysis and pleased that I finally had a term to describe certain aspects of my brain functioning: *I have been diagnosed with Pure O. I mean, it does have a certain ring to it right? Or does it? Pure O… Pure O… it doesn't slip off the tongue very easily. Also, having just the one part of a well-known diagnosis OCD is not ideal as it is like getting half of a diagnosis… but at least it is something. Besides, it beats my previous diagnosis of a personality disorder. Wait, have I officially been diagnosed with Pure O and is there actually such a thing as Pure O? Yes, Google has confirmed – Pure O is a form of OCD marked by repeated, intrusive, and uncontrollable thoughts (or obsessions) that are usually not accompanied by outward behavioural compulsions. However, this variant is not listed as a separate diagnosis in the DSM-5, the diagnostic manual used by many physicians, psychiatrists and psychologists.*

My psychologist, Claire, offered to meet for weekly therapy sessions at my local practice, to discuss my obsessions and find strategies for relieving the symptoms. During our first session she handed me what I can only describe as a child's workbook containing a sketch of someone with thought bubbles surrounding them. The person was supposed to represent me, and the bubbles were my thoughts. I was asked to keep a diary of my obsessive thoughts. Then, together, we would discuss methods to counteract these thoughts, in the hope of reducing the symptoms of Pure O. In theory, I understand the importance in being proactive in working with a psychologist to overcome such difficulties and it would be wrong for me to render this approach as invaluable. However, I lasted no more than two sessions for what I can only assume was because of my scepticism about the therapy on offer and a fundamental unwillingness to change. Allow me to elaborate… first of all, there was nothing written in the workbook that I did not already know. Common sense (although admittedly not my strong point) would tell you that if you are having negative thoughts, then one possible way to eliminate those thoughts is to engage in a sport or any kind of exercise that releases serotonin in the brain. While I completely agree with this (and I know there is much evidence to support this) I cannot help feeling that if it was really that simple, then surely, I would have resolved my issues before now.

Secondly, as we all know, ongoing, everlasting change requires effort and a commitment to make those changes. I did not have the drive, determination and desire to change my thoughts. Yes, I was struggling with life, and yes, I needed to make some changes but my repetitive and persistent thoughts allowed for escapism from the real world and, although they were distracting at times, they also offered me a deep sense of comfort.

I also have the mindset that my thoughts are so deeply embedded and inextricably linked with my identity that taking them away would take away a part of me. This leads me to my next point, which is more of a rhetorical question – can you really change your thoughts, or do you just suppress them? This is a controversial topic but if the latter were true, then it seemed possible that my thoughts would go away for a while then resurface, stronger and more resilient than ever. And, of course, this would defeat the purpose of the therapy.

Anyway, given my limited knowledge on the subject, I am not able to make any factual claims about how the brain processes information, and this is far from what I am trying to do. I am merely explaining my thought processes with the hope of putting some context to my decision, rightly or wrongly, to end the weekly sessions so soon.

Rock Bottom

My emotional outbursts in the workplace began to increase, often being triggered by feelings of anger and frustration. In a bid to escape, I started to go home during my shifts, which was a new development. I had become heavily dependent on Jenna for support, to the point where I guess you could say I had developed an obsession with her, albeit a different type of obsession to the infatuation I had had with Steve. It was the simple things like a hug, a reassuring comment or a text message that offered a level of comfort and safety beyond anything anyone else could give me.

You may be wondering: why her? Why didn't I go to my parents for support? I genuinely don't know the answer to this. Perhaps I felt she understood me in a way my family did not because she was, less emotionally involved than them in my life so it was easier for her to offer support when needed. Just being in her company, however briefly, was enough to eradicate my anxiety for a short period of time. However, this soon became a problem. You see, I sought Jenna's reassurance on a regular basis, like a drug, and the best way to obtain it was by becoming emotional.

I am not for one minute saying that I "put it on" or pretended to be upset in order to get attention: the feelings were very much real. It was more that I was not afraid to express my feelings in front of Jenna since she was the catalyst who enhanced my mood. However, it had become a vicious cycle whereby, the more she comforted me, the more I sought her support. I had become needy and I was increasingly aware of this.

Here is the thing, I know logically that my behaviour is irrational and that I am demonstrating a pattern of obsessive behaviour, mostly when it comes to other people. I am also aware of the possibility that I could scare these people away if they suspect my obsession; so I did my best to keep our communication to a minimum and only to communicate with her when it was being reciprocated, at least at first. However, my problems arise over time as the dependency evolves. At a certain point, I seem to lose all inhibition and control over my impulses and, eventually, the conversation becomes a little more one-sided and the support dwindles as a result.

However, to save myself from falling into a state of depression, I convince myself that the person genuinely cares about me and wants to help me, so they will understand and put up with my demanding behaviour for as long as it takes, irrespective of the fact they are married and have other commitments. In my head, the feelings are mutual, and I am always as much at the forefront of their mind, as they are for me. This is what keeps my fantasy alive.

I don't think I was wrong to believe that Jenna cared for me. I mean, she even left work to come to the doctor's with me, showing a real caring and nurturing side that was not so evident in the work environment. She could be hard when she needed to be – a managerial trait that I admire – but she was also kind and soft underneath the hardened exterior. Unfortunately, the area manager got wind of the situation: I believe she took a firm stance on the matter, suggesting that our relationship should be kept strictly professional.

On a couple of occasions when I was feeling overwhelmed by my emotions, I considered leaving, in search of a more challenging and fulfilling job. I even attempted to leave a few times. However, when I had calmed down and questioned my motives, I returned to work the following day.

My last and final attempt to leave work did result in me leaving for good, but not through a considered, well thought out process. It happened through impulse and with a different intention. In the long term, I did want to move on to bigger and better things, but because of my difficulty with change and my reliance on Jenna for support, I felt stuck in my current situation. Despite my previous empty threats, I knew deep down that I would never make the conscious, deliberate decision to leave my work. I say this at the risk of sounding like a terrible person: but to retain authenticity and be true to myself the truth is, I was only threatening to leave my work because I was struggling internally, and I wanted a reaction. Not just any reaction but a specific one that would build my self-esteem and make me feel valuable in the workplace. In spite of my preconceived notions, Jenna's response was unexpectedly assertive: a definitive, "Yes, I think it is time for you to leave".

I was dumbfounded! I stood there waiting for her to correct herself or to say that she had made a mistake, but she didn't. I was heartbroken, confused, lost and more importantly, I felt betrayed. I felt an immediate urge to escape, to go to bed and never wake up.

I would usually have caught the bus home from work, but I was not in the mood for people staring at me as I cried uncontrollably, so I booked a taxi instead. My parents were living in Spain over the summer and were not there to support me, not that I was bothered, since all I wanted to do, was retreat into myself without being bombarded with questions. My sister Cara, who was also living in my parent's house at the time, arrived home from work that evening, to find me distraught, and unable to move from my bed. She tried to console me, but it was useless. It was one of the worst moments in my life. I had lost my job and Jenna at the same time and, even worse, I had brought it on myself.

All I wanted to do was turn the clock back and do things differently. I tried to phone Jenna and even sent her a couple of messages, all without a response. I have no idea what they said at the time, but as I was emotional and feeling let down by her, I suspect they were not very pleasant. I do recall throwing accusations around and wanting to make her feel guilt and regret. At the same time, I was also pleading to be allowed to return to work and start afresh.

I could not understand how someone I cared about could dismiss me so abruptly and immediately. I started to question whether the feelings I had had towards her had not been reciprocated. One thing was for sure: she had made the decision to let me go and it didn't take long for me to realise that there was no going back this time.

How was I feeling during this sudden and unexpected turn of events? Quite simply, I was grieving a loss. Not just for Jenna, but for my job – a specific job, in an exact location in the centre where I belonged. The thought of living my life without those things was inconceivable.

How would I cope? What would I do? My routine as I knew it: gone! Jenna, my protection from the world outside my own little bubble: gone! Suddenly, I was exposed and vulnerable, with nothing and no one to cling on to for support. With all these uncertainties, I was no longer in control of my life, and I could not see a way forward. The anxiety was crippling, so much so that my dad returned from his extended holiday to offer his support.

I lay on the sofa in a state of… well… just a state, while my sister called the doctor. My family were deeply concerned about my state of mind and desperate to find a solution, one that would bring me out of the depths of depression and back into reality. I cannot recall what advice I was given but I am pretty certain that I was not admitted to hospital: the fact that I wasn't having suicidal thoughts meant that I was not in any immediate danger and I posed minimal risk to myself and others.

My dad and I caught a flight to Spain the following day and I spent a couple of weeks basking in the sun, while still feeling miserable and contemplating life. My parents were staying in a golfing resort in a small town called Los Alcázares, on the Mar Menor, and a short distance from Alicante. Their apartment was a short cycle ride away from the beach and I remember visiting the same café every day, to indulge in the homemade cakes. They were out of this world, offering a brief but mind-altering moment of pure happiness.

Surprisingly, it didn't take that long for me to change my mindset from "I am deeply depressed and want to stay in bed for the rest of my life" to "I am going to fight this and take back the control. I will prove to myself and others that I will not be defeated by my circumstances. I can and I will, be something! Now what shall I be?"

I spent the next few days on my laptop in the golf clubhouse searching for job vacancies and working on my CV. The search was of course, filtered to… wait for it… Aberdeen and Sales. Unfortunately, there was not an option whereby I could filter my search by location within a location, and narrow it down to my favourite shopping centre. I was presented with a list of job vacancies in less desirable locations. A Google Maps guide to the job vacancies would have been a helpful, efficient way to identify suitable jobs by their location and eliminate those in the wrong location. Then I could have tiered the job vacancies from "definitely could work in that location", to "possibly but would need repeated exposure to the area first", to "definitely not, not even for a position as the MD of the company on a ridiculously high salary".

One job caught my eye – Assistant Manager at a British-style clothing shop. It was a step up from my most recent position and although it was not located within the centre, it was only a short distance away. I tried to envisage myself working there, having this conversation with myself as I did: *How will I feel in that environment? It is hard to know since I have never been in the shop, but I am familiar with the external area. I could go to the centre for lunch each day, thus allowing me to create an association between my new job and the centre. The quickest way to enter the centre from there is via the Boots entrance – this is the same entrance I used during free periods at lunchtime when I was at school. As I do not want to be reminded of school, this will pose a problem. I could take the longer route, using the main entrance of the centre but this will eat into my lunch break. Nevertheless, it will be worth it. How many entrances does the shop have? Two: one entrance is within a small shopping centre and the other leads out to the cobbled street. I think I will feel more comfortable entering from the centre side, as it is closer to the Bon Accord Centre and further away from my school. What about the staff? I might not fit. Oh fuck it... I am going to apply and see what happens.*

I flew back to Aberdeen a couple of days later, in preparation for my job interview. I didn't get the job, but I wasn't surprised since I didn't really connect with the person interviewing me. To be honest, it felt less like a rejection and more like a weight had been lifted from my shoulders. It was a relief to dispose of all thoughts associated with the job and relax my mind for a short period of time. Something else would come up, something I was better suited to. I just had to bide my time, and that I did.

I was headhunted! Did you hear me? Yes, headhunted! One of the girls I had previously worked with contacted me to say that her manager had heard about my amazing sales ability (with specific reference to account opening) and was keen to have me on board at their store in Aberdeen. It was *Topshop*: a well-known clothing store for teenagers. I had always felt inferior to the fashion-conscious female staff there. Yet, I was about to become one of them.

More importantly, I would be working in the centre again, so I agreed without hesitation. I cannot remember what my title was but I know it was higher than sales assistant, as they had me working back of house, dealing with the financial aspects of the business as well as staff training, while working closely with the store manager. Additionally, I was clearly appreciated from day one. In fact, the manager seemed genuinely excited with her new recruit. On my first day working there, the manager pulled aside a male member of staff and asked me to give him a quick training session on how to open accounts. "Come on Francesca… tell him… tell him how you do it?" Caught off guard, I explained my sales tactic and they both seemed really impressed. I'm not sure it was so much what I said: it was perhaps more about the passion and determination in my presentation. Either way, they had put me on a pedestal and I wasn't going to complain about it.

The following day, I received a call from my manager at 9.30am. My shift was due to start at 9am but I had deliberately slept in, as I felt unable to get out of bed. I took the call and agreed to go in for a meeting with my boss in the afternoon. I felt guilty and ashamed. I did not want to let people down but my desire to please others was being overridden by my anxiety and a lack of motivation to get out of bed. In the absence of motivation, I wanted to close myself off from the outside world, with immediate effect and until further notice. Later that day, I went in as promised, to explain. I made it clear that I was not able to resume my role and had no option but to leave, permanently. My manager was accepting but clearly not pleased, perhaps even disappointed. She no doubt felt let down by me. Anyway, that was the premature end of my days of being headhunted, so it was onto the next chapter of my life, whatever that entailed.

There was no time for procrastination and it was time to move forward: I must have been feeling momentarily positive. Right, so where did I go from there? I had pretty much exhausted all my options in the centre. I considered the possibility of working in a retail store elsewhere and, although this was an anxiety-provoking idea, it was not out of the question. I was back to the vicious circle of questions. After ruminating on work issues, I decided that I needed another focus… so I decided to join a dating site again in the hope that I might develop an interest in someone who was not Steve. Please, anyone but Steve!

More Than Me

Rich was much better looking than my usual type, aka Steve – dark hair, brown eyes, nice smile, strong facial features, prominent cheek bones and clean-shaven. With only one photo uploaded for public viewing, he seemed good looking but not vain. Moreover, his personal profile matched my perception of the person in the photo: sensible, grounded, mature (for his age), intelligent and the opposite of a player. He didn't say these words exactly, but I was able to glean this from his self-description. For example, he described his interests without referring to his skills or achievements. This told me that he was confident in his own abilities without feeling the need to boast about them. Either that or he did not have any skills.

However, given his interests were web design, cooking and computing, this seemed highly unlikely. He mentioned that he lived by himself, suggesting a level of maturity and independence. There was no mention of his physique and he would consider dating someone who was slim, athletic or a little overweight. This told me that he was open-minded, since he was not basing his search solely on appearance. He did not claim to be a nice guy (I hate this) and refrained from using humour to sell himself (no need for someone who is quietly confident). Finally, his profile was short, concise, and exempt of emotion: even subtle emotions that some people portray through kisses, emojis and exclamation marks. So it was all adding to my sense of intrigue. Despite my aversion to commitment, fuelled by my fear of relationships, I quickly decided that if it was ever going to happen, it would be with him, and this time I meant it. No time for small talk, which in my mind is futile anyway. Besides, I knew everything I needed to know at this point.

I made the initial contact: "Fancy going to the cinema?" "When?" "Tonight?" "Sure".

We started dating and after a short six months, I fell pregnant. It was an unexpected but welcome surprise – note the juxtaposition between welcome and surprise, two words that I rarely use in the same sentence. Suddenly, without warning, my life was about to change drastically. Yet somehow, I felt calm and excited about embracing my new life without hesitation or regret about my decision to keep the pending child. Within the first few months of my pregnancy, I took the next logical step by moving out of my parents' house and into Rich's flat. It was the first time I had lived away from home and although the transition was mentally challenging, I felt that it was something I had to do: as a symbol of commitment to our relationship.

Being pregnant was a strange but comforting sensation. I felt more confident than ever, and for a number of reasons. One of these was that having an additional person inside me made me feel whole, complete and more secure in this unpredictable world. For the first time since I had turned 16, I did not feel under pressure to work, which was conducive to a healthier, more relaxed state of mind. I also received special treatment for being pregnant, as random people acknowledged me and commented on my bump while boosting my ego by commenting on my healthier appearance. I had become vulnerable, almost childlike but, at the same time, I felt like a proper adult. I was vulnerable in the sense that there was an overwhelming desire, not just from me, but also from my family, to protect the baby.

There were also the logistical issues associated with having a big bump in the latter months, forcing me to go slow and restricting me from carrying out basic tasks (an excuse to be lazy if ever there was one). I felt like an adult because: a) at 24 I suppose I was actually an adult; b) carrying a child is a huge responsibility and it requires a certain amount of maturity (or ignorance) to embrace it; and c) having a child demonstrated a willingness to put someone else first for the first time in my life, which was more akin to adult behaviour. I also felt feminine, simply because men cannot carry babies, thus making me feel more natural about my gender. My hair got thicker and my skin was miraculously smooth and glowing. No longer did I feel inferior to those *Topshop* girls – I could comfortably shop in such environments, anxiety-free, during my entire pregnancy. More importantly, I did not have to pretend to be something I was not. I was going to be a mum and I was content with my newfound identity. I can honestly say that my new status as a mum to be was working for me – thank fuck, as something had to.

The birth was nothing short of a miracle. I relished my 36 hours in labour, which was by far my biggest challenge to date. I had developed a rash prior to the birth: more specifically, it was a polymorphic light eruption, a pregnancy rash that occurs in under 1% of pregnancies and usually presents itself during the third trimester, especially during the last five weeks. It was an extremely itchy rash and topical steroids did little to relieve the symptoms. The Itchy And Scratchy Show continued morning, noon and night and disrupted our sleep for several days prior to the onset of labour.

I think Rich was at the end of his tether – and rightly so – as we were both physically and mentally exhausted from sleep deprivation. Yet the mental impact of this was partly suppressed by adrenalin, the result of mental anticipation and excitement about our future.

The contractions started around 5pm on Saturday the 13th of March 2011. They were mild, slightly uncomfortable but not painful, lasting 20 to 30 seconds and approximately 20 minutes apart. By 7pm, the contractions were much the same, perhaps a little more regular but nothing more than the kind of slight discomfort that could be endured by the weakest of souls. I was beginning to think that *One Born Every Minute* was staged as it certainly wasn't representative of my experience thus far. 8pm: *Oh fuck, that was a sore one.* It was similar to a bout of bad cramp associated with irritable bowel syndrome or the type you get after eating six slices of white bread before bedtime. 8.30pm: I wondered how long it would take until the baby arrived. This question was quickly followed by hypothetical "what if" scenarios: *What if the baby is really ugly and I cannot connect with it? Bit late now... better not tell Rich what I am thinking... he will be really ang... ahhhh! Fuck, shit, fuck, shit... ooh that was sore AND STILL GOING ON... 38, 39, 40 and breathe. Hopefully not much longer now since I am beginning to dislike this experience.* 9pm: "Rich, you should go to bed for a couple of hours since we are going to be up during the night". 9.30pm: *Oh God, why did I send Rich to bed. I am in complete agony and the contractions are getting closer together.* I was so tired I felt my eyes momentarily closing between contractions. The contractions were still almost one minute apart but each one was lasting 30 to 40 seconds and intensifying in pain. 10pm: *FUCK THIS!* "Rich, wake up!" The tears were streaming down my face. I could not cope any longer: I thought I might die if I endured any more pain (dramatic, I know). I needed to go to hospital immediately. We phoned the neonatal ward of the hospital and requested permission to go in. They agreed, tentatively, but also made it clear I might be sent home again since my contractions were still far apart. I decided to take my chances, even if it only served as a distraction from the pain. 11pm: After a quick vaginal inspection, the midwife confirmed 4 cm dilation, just over the threshold for hospital admission. My hind waters had not yet burst – yes, apparently, we have multiple "waters" that burst during labour – and required a little bit of prodding to quicken the process. 2am: The midwife ushered me through to a room where the anaesthetist was waiting, ready to insert the epidural. However, I was stopped in my tracks, bent over in excruciating pain. The midwife obviously pre-empted my next move as she quickly assisted me to the nearest toilet, where I threw up. 3am: The anaesthetist asked me to stay still while she inserted the needle into my spine. It seemed to take forever, possibly because I was having contractions while kneeling in an upright position on the bed, all while trying not to move my body or throw up.

IT DIDN'T WORK… the epidural that is! I don't know if I accidentally moved or if the needle wasn't inserted correctly, but either way, I had to retain my position for longer, while in complete agony. 4am: The process was repeated with success. Just as well, as I was really beginning to struggle, both physically and mentally. My body was weak and I was suffering from exhaustion. 5.00am: It didn't take long for the wonder drug to work its magic. My body was numb and pain-free, except for the odd twinge from time to time. My midwife had finished her shift and been replaced by another, equally experienced midwife who popped into the room from time to time to examine me.

The next couple of hours were reasonably calm –Rich was trying to sleep in a chair in the corner of the room while I tried to doze off, but my body would not allow for it. There was calming music being played that created some ambience and enhanced our chilled mood. 10:00am: No changes. 1:00pm: Third midwife on shift and still no baby. 5.00pm: A nurse checked up on me and accidentally knocked the epidural stand, which led to a subsequent interruption of the flow of medicine into my body. I was none the wiser until… arggghh, the pain had returned. This time I was too weak to fight it. My entire body was shaking and my temperature was rising. My midwife, who was all for natural births, suggested I battle on through without medication. Now I am all for taking the natural approach where possible, and I did consider rising to the challenge... but... my body and mind were screaming at me in parallel... EPIDURAL, EPIDURAL, TAKE THE FUCKING EPIDURAL. I felt like I was going to die, my baby would die, we would both die. "Whatever you think, I trust your judgement". So, she left me to it, to endure the most unbearable pain I had ever experienced. Dare I say it, the physical ramifications of being in labour possibly trumped the acute mental pain of feeling anxious. 8pm: *Get this fucking baby out of me! This is much worse than anything I have seen on* One Born Every Fucking Minute. 24 hours in labour with zero sleep – my mind was too far gone to feel anxious, but my body was failing me. 8:10pm: Two doctors and several nurses crowded around my bed. "She has developed a fever. For goodness sake, someone fix the epidural back onto the wall". I was relieved when the assertive doctor took control of the situation. Then he turned to me "We need to check the baby is okay. I am going to scrape the baby's head if that is alright with you". The feeling of embarrassment from farting in the doctor's face was quickly replaced by fear and panic when he announced: "Your baby is really ill; we need to get it out now". 8:30pm: The doctor considered carrying out a C-section but, as the epidural was working again and my temperature had reduced, he was prepared to wait an hour or so to see if I could deliver the baby naturally. I was at this point 9 cm dilated and almost ready to push. 10pm: Almost a full day and a half since my first contraction. 'Okay Francesca it's time to push this baby out'.

Pushing was by far the easiest part of being in labour; my lower body was numb, and I had little feeling down below – thank goodness for small mercies. The exit point was not big enough for the baby's great big head to escape, so the midwife carefully (or not so carefully, but I was none the wiser) made an incision to widen the exit. At this point, she could have ripped out my insides and I would not have cared. Whatever it took to get the baby out. I continued to push for ten minutes or so until, "come on Francesca, one last push" … and… "is he here", I asked? I couldn't see past the bloodbath. But I had a baby boy! Born at 11pm on Sunday the 14th March 2011. We didn't know the sex beforehand, but I had just known I was having a boy. Mother's instinct? Nah, not really. It was the rash that gave it away. I had read somewhere that polymorphic eruption is caused by hormonal changes during pregnancy and is more common when carrying males. Whether this is true or not I do not know. It is however, my rationalisation for having predicted the sex of my son, Oscar.

It is true to say that I felt unconditional love for Oscar from the moment he was born. He came straight out the womb and onto the breast, which ensured the formation of an instant bond. He gave me a new sense of purpose, one that went beyond me, myself and I. For the first time in my life, I was responsible for someone and I wanted to protect him, and to shield him against the external world. Prior to Oscar's birth, I had been concerned that I would feel indifferent towards my own child. I had been exposed to babies in the past and, while other people were brooding over them, I had been disinterested, and reluctant to pretend otherwise.

I do wonder if people show other people's babies such extreme interest because it is deemed to be socially appropriate rather than because they are genuinely fascinated by the newborn. But then you hear people ask to hold the child, even look after it! Surely that goes beyond social pressure, and suggests a genuine interest in the child that is not their own? In fact, I would even go as far as to say that most new-born babies, despite having features that are supposed to render them cute, are ugly... and sometimes very ugly indeed.

My baby was of course, an exception to the rule… he was adorable… Funny how everyone loves their own baby, regardless of what pops out of them. There must be an innate predisposition to love your own child no matter what. Of course, I fully acknowledge that not everyone is the same. This was my personal experience and while not everyone feels the same way as I do (hard to believe but I am told its true), I am sure that the majority of parents will relate to this.

Parenting is difficult. Do not believe anyone who tells you otherwise. I love my son, of course I do, but raising a child is tedious and incredibly wearing, particularly during the first six months. Sleep deprivation was by far the biggest factor in affecting my mood and significantly amplifying my anxiety. I was feeling constantly tired, irritable and anxious. And I was very aware that I had no means of escaping my duties as a mother, a breastfeeding mother.

On average, Oscar demanded a "milky feed" between three and six times per night, and this continued for several months. It was relentless. To be woken out of a deep sleep is disorientating and deeply frustrating, and it was happening multiple times every night. I swear it almost killed me. Just when you think the baby has gone back to sleep and you can finally get some rest, they start crying again and are back on the breast for some consoling (I think it is often as much a request to be comforted as to be fed).

I often woke up in the morning, claiming to be "shattered and desperate for a good nap": a bad habit that I have to admit has stayed with me, since my nine-year-old son can no longer be held responsible for my inability to sleep. Every day during the first few months was like Groundhog Day. Staying indoors was not an option for my sanity and I often found myself walking aimlessly around, unable to think coherently and willing my baby to fall asleep in the pram so I could catch some rest. I would spend hours trying to get Oscar to sleep until, after a lot of grafting and perseverance, he would occasionally doze off in my arms. A wave of relief came over me as I could sense a well-earned rest on the horizon. I gently put him in his cot and quietly lay down on the sofa beside him, praying for a long-lasting nap to recharge the brain, until… five fucking minutes! *How is that even possible? He was out for the count six minutes ago. This is a deliberate attempt to challenge me, to remind me that parenthood is the hardest job in the world.*

Tears would be streaming down my face as I reluctantly picked him up and popped him back on the breast, while he would pretend to be asleep as he sucked all the goodness out of my breasts. I watched in amazement as my breasts transformed from full bazookas to something that resembled empty potato sacks, dangling by my belly button. The things you do for your children eh?

Rich and I split when Oscar was eight months old. Out of respect for Oscar and his father, this is all I have to say on the matter. I moved back in with my parents for a few short months before spreading my wings and gaining some much-needed independence. I relocated to a small village on the outskirts of the city, well away from my past and the mentally tarnished areas that provoked my anxiety. So in a way, it was yet another form of escapism. The property was located on a narrow lane, with little in the way of outdoor lighting and few properties nearby, so it didn't give me that feeling of safety and security I usually relied on.

It was a self-contained cottage on two levels: an old stone house that was always dark even with the lights on, and always cold even with the heating on. It, or rather something, made strange noises that I could only attribute to the presence of a ghost or living creature of some sort. If you are anything like me (unlikely I know), then everything feels worse at night. I don't know the exact reason for this but I do sometimes wonder if it has something to do with natural light deprivation: maybe that is what triggers my anxiety. Anyway, my point is that any feelings of anxiety, depression or isolation were magnified significantly when I was in the cottage, especially at night. At bedtime, I developed a simple routine to enhance my safety and alleviate my anxiety. First and foremost, I ensured the front and back doors were locked (I feel the need to state this point since this is something we never did while I was growing up, so it was a novel experience). I removed all of the plugs from the walls to prevent a fire, switched off all of the lights as quickly as possible then ran upstairs before the monstrous creature caught me or I died from a heart attack triggered by fear.

Once I was upstairs, I was relatively safe, and I would fall asleep quickly, too afraid to move once I was firmly tucked up in bed. If I woke up during the night, needing the toilet, tough. It would have to wait until the morning. Fortunately, by this time, Oscar had started sleeping right through the night. Just as well really, as I could easily have been too scared to attend to him, despite sleeping in the same room.

One particular night, I woke up at 3am to the sound of creaking floorboards and a muffled voice, suggesting that someone or something other than Oscar and me, was in the cottage. *First thing to do in a crisis of this nature – check son is still in cot. Phew. Next. Hide under the covers and do not move until the suspected burglar disappears.* The noises continued for a good ten minutes or so before I heard the back door close, followed by silence. I went straight back to sleep, too frightened to do anything else.

In the morning, I went downstairs and found a note at my kitchen sink. Apparently, my back door had been left wide open and my neighbour had entered the property after a night out to: a) alert me; and b) close the door. I smirked to myself as I processed the reality of what had happened. I mean, forgetting to lock the door is one thing, but forgetting to shut it? That is quite something, even for me.

I was lonely, possibly even depressed, during my time living in the village. I also felt extremely uncomfortable in my immediate environment, the place I was supposed to call home. It was as if my identity had somehow been removed and temporarily put somewhere else, waiting for me to get through whatever it was I was going through, and find myself again. I despised not just the cottage, but also the entire village in which I was residing. I felt so out of place, like a lost girl in a cliquey little farmers' village, where everyone knew one another, and the formation of tight well-formed groups made it difficult for any newcomers to permeate the community. It was a place where everyone had a synchronised dress code (Barbour jackets or tweed coats and Hunter wellies) and their own moral code of conduct. They were friendly with one another but wary of people outside their own group and reluctant to acknowledge anyone who did not resemble one of their own.

I made the effort to become included by taking Oscar to a toddler group in my local area (God I hate those groups). Can you believe that not one person even acknowledged me? There I was, back to being invisible, feeling like a complete gooseberry, sitting in the corner pretending to play with my son, while all the other "local" mothers were chatting among themselves. There was of course a smidgeon of a chance that I played a part in the lack of communication with the other mothers at toddler group: I have, in the past, been described as showing apparently aloof mannerisms in social situations. Poor eye contact also supports this impression, so it is possible that I failed to acknowledge other people who might have been prepared to engage with me.

Regardless of whether this was the case or not, it certainly didn't feel that way at the time. I felt like a child in the school playground, the one who is inferior to everyone else, the uncool kid who no one wants to be associated with. Did I go back to toddler group?

Of course not. Why would I subject myself or my son to that nonsense, when we were quite happy doing our own thing, in our own way?

It didn't take long for me to succumb to my desire to escape the village I had escaped to in the first place. I swallowed my pride (not that I had had much to begin with) by moving out of the property and back in with my parents a couple of months before my six-month tenancy was due to expire. I was spending increasingly more time away from the cottage and it seemed pointless to continue using it as a halfway house, for the sake of demonstrating some independence, when I didn't really care what people thought anyway. Besides, the cost of paying a couple of month's rent for an empty property was minimal compared to the benefits for my mental health of moving out.

Being back living with my mother, only this time under different circumstances, with a child added to the mix, was... well... how do I put this politely? Uncompromisingly difficult, for both of us. Actually... no... that is not quite right... it was... fucking horrific! We argued frequently and often felt a burning desire to kill one another, quite literally, I can assure you. I suspect part of the problem is our similar yet opposing natures. We are both impulsive and driven by our emotions. Yet one is eccentric, sociable, a mix of authoritarian and authoritative style of parenting, while the other is quietly reserved (in certain situations), socially inept at times and has a more permissive style of parenting. The opposition of this concoction of traits is sure to ignite the fire.

To give you a better idea of what I mean, here are some of my mum's recurring phrases about what she perceived as wrongdoings on my part: "You must stop napping Francesca, you have responsibilities now. You have been in all day, it is not good for you or your son, he needs fresh air. You must stop moaning and get on with it.

I raised four children, while looking after two students at the same time. Why is he not wearing a jacket and a hat? It is freezing outside. Why is he not wearing shorts? It is the summer and he needs the fresh air around his legs".

My standard responses to my mother's rants included: "I am shattered, will you watch Oscar while I sleep? I am too tired to go out just now, I have been up half of the night. I will go out later, after my nap. I love my son unconditionally, but this job is so tedious, I have no life of my own. He is wearing two bloody layers, that is sufficient for any human being. I don't wear shorts so why the hell would I subject my son to wearing shorts?"

My mum won of course – I would go out because I was too scared to stay in. The jacket, hat, and even a cover ensured that Oscar was cocooned in his buggy and my mum was left feeling satisfied.

In spite of how this sounds, we did also have good times living together too. We laughed, a lot, often because my mum was making fun of my dad or vice versa or because she was doing something silly, like throwing the wet washing over the balcony, in the hope that it would land on the whirligig below, thus saving her the effort of having to go downstairs. We never fought during mealtimes. In fact, it is one of the few times when there was complete silence in the Baird household. For other families, eating together provides a time to be connected, when families converse and enjoy each other's company. We, on the other hand, viewed mealtime as a separate entity, one where we were focused on our food, and only on our food.

Why would I want to communicate while I am fully immersed in the process of eating? Unless of course, I did not like the meal and was using communication as a delaying tactic to avoid eating it. However, I can never imagine this being the case with me.

A Healthier Obsession

I have this terrible way of reverting into a childlike mode when I am with my mother, allowing her to dominate and take control of situations while I kick back and shun all responsibility. To be back living with my parents at the age of 25 was doing nothing for my confidence or my independence. It is therefore not surprising that after a short three or four months living under my parents' roof, I decided to move out and regain some much-needed independence.

My dad spotted an advertisement in a local shop for the rental of a property in the same village as them. The flat was ideally located, as it was situated on the main road approximately 100 yards from my parents' house. As soon as I entered the flat, I instantly felt comfortable and as though my identity was once again intact. It was a bright and spacious (but not too spacious), modern flat in a great location in the heart of the village, with plenty of amenities nearby. The main attraction had to be the large glass double doors that overlooked the main road, with a stunning view of the hills and countryside beyond. All the rooms were of a proportionate size and finished to a high standard. It was in a block of seven other flats, and being on the second floor, gave me a sense of security and protection from the outside world. It was exactly what I needed at that time in my life, so I signed the tenancy agreement with a week or so to prepare for the big move.

At this stage, the sudden realisation that I had made a commitment triggered feelings of fear and panic and eroded any positive emotions I had been feeling up until that point. I should have known better. Why would I cope well with this life-changing experience when I had failed to do so with so many others? The entire context of my life was about to change significantly, requiring the formation of a new sense of self. How does one adjust to changes that are loaded with unknowns, which create so much uncertainty? I have never understood how people can just move to a different home, a different area or a different country without having a nervous breakdown. There must be a grieving process that accompanies this, for the life lost that is never to return. Surely, that person would lose their identity in the process? Or do people have a core identity that is unyielding, even in the face of such adversity? Perhaps their identity is bound up with the people they are with, or maybe they are excited to form a new one? I find this hard to believe. I feel their identity must somehow be intertwined with the context in which they operate, just as it is for me. The idea of anything else is, frankly, unfathomable to me.

I felt a strong urge to control my environment and I was desperately trying to construct mental associations between the flat and all of the other aspects of my life. It was like I was trying to fit all of the pieces of a jigsaw puzzle together. In the process, I imagined the flat, and Oscar and me living in the flat, and considered how it would impact on the wider context of my life. It would be a new permanent home and therefore serve as the foundations of my life.

I imagined it to be a bit like a spider diagram with the home at the centre of it, where my identity would be firmly embedded: the arms and legs of the spider were formed by everything else on the peripheral. In some respects, being in a position of limbo made the prospect of change easier to digest. The only constant in my life at that time was Oscar, so I had nothing to lose by making such a life-affirming change. Yet, at the same time, my life was precarious and fragile, devoid of meaning beyond Oscar.

I often think of my life as a structure, made of building blocks, with one strategically placed on top of the other. If one of those building blocks breaks, the entire structure crumbles. Another way of looking at it is through the notion that my sense of self is bound by interconnected parts that form a greater whole: I function best when all of the parts are formed and operating correctly, in a pre-defined and specific manner. If one of the connections fails or is temporarily interrupted, the individual parts do not work well in-dependently and the entire construct is destroyed. As I have said before, my sense of self – which is imperative for my well-being – is a mental construct and a fantasy world, formed within the context of my environment. It is also inextricably linked with my perception of how certain others perceive me as I navigate my way through my environment.

At this time in my life, I was jobless, single, hobbyless and with-out an obsession of any sort, so my home was an important piece of the puzzle when it came to reconstructing the building blocks of my life. It was therefore imperative to make the right decision – whether to move or not. I spent the following week weighing up the pros and cons of the physical move, as I needed to determine whether this was the correct course of action for me and my de-pendent son. Just a week later, I had made my decision, and moved out of my parent's house into the flat.

It didn't take long for Oscar and me to settle into our new living quarters. In the end, in spite of my worries, it just felt right. Apart from the obvious justification for this – it was a nice modern flat in a safe and secure environment – there was something else, something that could not be defined in words. What I am saying is that I simply do not know why some places are significantly favour-able to others. I suspect the answer to this lies within the deeper realms of the unconscious mind. Just as anxiety becomes greater with repeated exposure to areas I am not comfortable in, the oppo-site emotions are strengthened by places I do have deep and well formed connections with. Perhaps this is the reason I was feeling positive towards the new flat.

Whatever the reason was, I felt comfortable and positive about the move. Throughout my life, and even to this day, I have struggled to understand why I can deal with some major life changes and the context they are set in, while other seemingly trivial situations can cause me such difficulties and pain. Having thought deeply about my responses in certain situations, I have come to the conclusion that my mind is rigid and inflexible, and therefore unwilling to alter predefined emotions triggered by my location and events. To try and change my perception and ultimately my feelings within a context is a scary prospect, one that invokes severe anxiety to even contemplate. It would require a huge amount of mental adjustment to my preconceived notions. To do so would, in turn, confuse me, create unpredictability, and make it harder for me to manage my environment. So, I ask myself, even if I could make these changes, would I even want to?

The same applies to any decisions I make, whether consciously or not: they tend to be consistent, have longevity and to be unalterable. Once my mind is set, it will not be swayed by conflicting views or social pressures. Even when things don't go as planned or the statistical chance of success is low, I persevere either until I have accomplished my goal or can no longer pursue it because of circumstances that are beyond my control. In fact, as I have said before the lower my chances of success, the more determined I am to succeed. The next stage of my life perfectly exemplifies this tendency.

I think some anecdotal evidence will be useful here. Just before the demise of my relationship with Rich, I randomly decided to start an eBay business selling dust plugs: you know the little plugs that go into the headphone and charger port of your phone to prevent dust from entering them? No – you probably don't. Neither did

I until I stumbled across them on a Chinese selling website called DHGate.com. I had already made the decision to buy and sell on eBay (and you know what happens when I have my mind set on doing something). The product part of the process was, however, still an unknown. I looked at several products – mostly phone accessories, storage devices and batteries, all on Chinese selling websites, before settling on the "popular dust plug".

The product selection process was wholly influenced by four factors: availability of parts, price, supply and demand. This is where things begin to get interesting for me – if there is one thing I love talking about, it is money, or more accurately how to make money. Step 1: *Is there a demand for this product?* The number of listings and the number of sales is the best indicator. A low number of listings (supply) combined with a high number of sales (demand) is the best possible scenario as it makes it easier to compete in a "niche" market. Step 2: Determine the purchase price and check availability and lead time. The dust plugs were listed at 0.08 pence (priced per unit, with a minimum order quantity of 50). The delivery charge was determined by the weight and dimensions of the total order. So, for 100 plugs, I determined a cost of £8 + £10 for delivery + 30% duty; a charge incurred by the courier. This brought the total purchase price to £20.40. Keeping 1000s in stock and the availability of delivery with DHL or FedEx in 2-3 working days, ensured a quick turnaround to meet a possible increase in demand. Step 3: Determine a competitive selling price. Now this task is not as easy as it sounds: the best approach is to break it down into a number of sub-steps. Step 3.1: Work out the optimum selling price on eBay. In terms of supply and demand, I noted a positive correlation between the price (low) and number of sales (although this is not as simple as it seems, since images and other factors contribute to a seller's success rate). 0.99p for 1 pair of dust plugs plus 0.99p for delivery equated to the cheapest and most successful seller, providing a baseline for me to work with. Step 3.2: Determine my overhead costs for selling on eBay (including eBay fees, PayPal fees, postage price, and the cost of an envelope). There are less obvious other overheads such as electricity and wages which I also tried to factor in. Step 3.3: Set the price. I worked out that if, for every sale, I sold two sets instead of one, I could combine postage, thus reducing my costs. I estimated the total cost (including overheads) for each sale, at two pairs per sale, to be £1.70. A selling price of £1.89 + 99p delivery, would generate a profit of £1.18 and make me the cheapest seller on eBay, per unit ordered. It seemed like the kind of thing people would buy two of… I mean I wouldn't even buy one pair but, you know, other people might. Step 4: Carry out a miniature supplier appraisal. Supplier reviews… Trustpilot 3.5 out of 5. That will do nicely. Step 5: Place an order then wait, not so patiently, for the goods to arrive.

It was the longest two days of my life. I somehow managed to refrain from listing the items prior to receipt of goods, possibly because of Rich's stabilising influence. When the goods arrived, they were marked as a gift and thus no duty had been incurred. It was a promising start. Rich, who has a degree in web design, helped me to create a unique image to incorporate into my listing. I copied some spiel from a website, set the price, uploaded the picture and boom, my business was up and running. One hour later, having checked my phone approximately fifty times to see if there had been a sale, I heard a "kerching" (like the sound a till makes when it opens) followed by a notification on my phone: eBay, you have a sale!

I was having palpitations, but this time for the right reasons. I was jumping around ecstatically. *It worked, it worked. I have a sale.* This is where I think I differ from most people. I suspect most people's internal dialogue would have gone more like this, "Great I have a sale, but it's only one sale and I don't want to get carried away.

Let's just see what happens next". By contrast, I instantly thought, "This is going to be a success, I am a success".

I saw absolutely no room for pessimism or scepticism at this time. I only had thoughts of success as I eagerly contemplated the possibility of turning that one sale into a full-time business, perhaps even making millions over a short period of time. I felt I had demonstrated my entrepreneurial flare and that this might be the opportunity to pull me back from a lifetime of failure. A couple of hours later and there was another "kerching". I quickly prepared my deliveries, ready to dispatch them the following day. After a sleepless night, I woke up to another couple of sales and I just knew I was onto something great.

The eBay venture was not the first time I had lived with "my head in the clouds" and it certainly wouldn't be the last. Either way, I was happy and I wasn't prepared to let anyone disillusion me.

The grief and pain from losing Rich and my life as I knew it was insurmountable. Yet, I had become resilient. Possibly because I had learned to convert negative emotions into something positive and useful: in this instance the passion, drive, and determination to succeed in business. As the business began to expand, I required more equipment and increased space to support the growth. I bought a great big industrial-sized folding table which I initially set up in my parents' living room: it subsequently followed me to the cottage, back to my parents and up to the "new" flat – a status coined by Oscar to distinguish our current property and the previous homes. All of my profits were reinvested back into the business and, after a short two to three months, I was selling dust plugs in multiple colours and had even branched out with diamante dust plugs for those fashion-conscious individuals who like to dress up their phone.

The feedback was approximately 99.8% positive and as the sales continued to grow, I quickly made my way to the top of the listings (which is like being the first company that comes up in a Google search). Over the month of December, I had approximately 20 to 30 sales per day. To remain competitive, while enhancing profitability, I introduced a multi-buy deal: three sets of dust plugs for the price of two. This deal proved to be extremely popular and increased my profits per sale quite substantially.

Much to my mum's despair, my desk looked like Santa's grotto, with envelopes, sticky labels and a wide array of dust plugs creating an unwanted distraction and mess in my parents' living room. This coupled with the mess created by an eight-month-old baby and, even more so, his mother, was sure to drive my mum insane. I was quite happy to take the mess elsewhere, where I would not be condemned or made to feel guilty for being me: since I perceive my mess as a symptom of how my cluttered mind works.

After approximately six months of what I would deem as an unbelievable amount of sales for something so unfathomably popular, other sellers caught on to the hot selling product. This resulted in increased competition and an inevitable reduction in my sales. I did not want to give up on my hot potato so, in order to remain competitive in a fast-growing market, I hired a franking machine, thus reducing the cost of postage. There was, of course, a monthly fee for this but after a quick calculation, I worked out that I could reduce my price by about 10%, cover the fees and still return a healthy profit, even with the reduction in sales. This seemed to work for a while, as I managed to retain a large percentage of my customers, while maintaining good profit. However, just like everything in life, it was not going to last forever, and I was soon forced to consider other avenues. At one stage I was selling a wide array of items including: phone covers, designer clothing, batteries, and storage devices (SDHC cards for cameras and phones). However, I struggled to turn over anywhere near the same profits with these items as I had done with dust plugs, suggesting that the money-making process was not as easy as I had originally anticipated.

Just as I was beginning to hit a brick wall, I found a great deal on branded memory cards, one that was sure to make a healthy return on my initial investment. I transferred £2,000 (most of my profits) to some dude in Malaysia and waited in anticipation for the goods to arrive. Can you imagine my disappointment and frustration when I opened the surprisingly light box, only to find... nada?

It took me a moment to consider the possibility that I had been scammed. I was trusting, naïve and had not considered the possibility that someone would lie to me in such a heartless way. *How could someone do this to me? All that hard-earned money lost in an instant, and all because of my stupidity*! I felt nauseous. I sent him numerous emails over a period of two weeks:

Email number 1: Dear Taj, it appears that you have made an error with my order. I have received an empty box – see picture below. Please can you kindly send me the memory cards I have paid for. Failing that, I will happily accept a full refund. Hope this issue can be rectified quickly. Awaiting your response. Kind Regards, Francesca.

At this point, I half believed, or at least I wanted to believe that he could have been silly enough to forget to put the goods in the box before they sent it (I mean, it is the type of thing I might do). Two days later there was no response. A slightly different approach this time: less of the innocence and more of a deliberate attempt to plead with his conscience:

Email number 2: I am a single mum on benefits (fact), and I rely on my hard-earned money to support myself and my child. Please, please can you rectify this issue. I am deeply distressed. Francesca.

A couple of days passed and I had still not received a response. In an echo of the way I had acted previously with both Steve and Jenna, I now became aggressive in my tone, demanding answers.

Email number 3: Where are your morals? Do you even have a conscience? I have contacted the police and the UK embassy in your country of residence. Be assured that further action will be taken. You have one last chance to redeem yourself or there will be consequences.

I just wanted a reaction, any reaction. To be honest, I half expected him to be amused by my threatening email, possibly even to shrug it off with a belittling remark. Much to my surprise, my more assertive, albeit petulant approach had an impact. He responded to my email almost instantly (just as well as I was already writing the next email which included several expletives). He apologised and tried to appease me by offering a partial refund. True to his word (on this occasion only) he refunded some of the money I had lost, in three instalments, several months apart. I accepted these refunds with gratitude, as if he was somehow doing me a favour – like giving me free money.

Having lost a significant percentage of my earnings to the scammer with a conscience, I had lost motivation and belief in my ability to succeed as an entrepreneur. Over the next six months, I continued to sell and make a small profit from selling dust plugs. However, my business was on the wane, much like my entrepreneurial flare. I sold job lots of stock at cost price, sometimes even less, to convert liquid assets into much needed cash: subsequently pushing my company, Littleladyfcb, into administration.

Without the adrenaline and "mental buzz" I had been obtaining from buying and selling, life once again became mundane: I was almost on the verge of becoming "normal". My head was firmly, albeit temporarily, out of the clouds and I was back living in the real world.

"Normal" Life

As you are now probably aware, I can deal with challenges and set-backs in life, but one thing I am not so good at is embracing "normality". I can live with it for a couple of days before panic kicks in and, for the sake of my health, I have no option but to revert to a fantasy world, and this time was no different. I was in desperate need of a goal, something I could obsess over, to stimulate my mind and create that much sought-after sense of comfort and control. However, this comfort and control comes with its own set of rules, since my special interests are often so specific and unhealthy, possibly even unattainable.

I am sorry to say it (much to my parents' disappointment), but the status quo – tidying my flat, cooking nice meals and spending my hard earned cash on a holiday that only serves to exasperate my anxiety due to a change to my routine – just won't do it for me. According to my father, becoming a well rounded person (one who is skilled in a lot of different things) equates to success. On that premise, if this is true, then, to be blunt, I am fucked.

I am definitely someone who knows a little about something and nothing about a lot. I have narrow interests and I am not prepared to escape my comfort zone to obtain a little knowledge about any subject that is unrelated to my current goal or obsession. Moreover, I would have thought that to become a well rounded individual, you must have a thirst for knowledge about an array of topics and be able to and want to prioritise your time to allow for such learning. I suspect this requires a myriad of comprehensive attributes, such as versatility and having a flexible and broad mind, all of which I lack. I operate in a very haphazard way and my priorities are, as some would argue, skewed (although they don't seem that way to me). Tasks that people deem as essential, and which perhaps contribute to the development of a well-rounded person, are at the bottom of my to do list.

To be honest, I do not have the time to engage in what I perceive as mundane tasks, like tidying and cooking. Well that's not strictly true – I enjoy cooking under very specific conditions: I must be alert (a rarity in my case as I am usually sleep deprived); a new recipe is usually required (it needs to be a challenge); the cooking must take place on a weekend (since I am always shattered after work); I must have plenty of money to buy all of the ingredients (usually just after payday or having won a bet); and finally, I must have nothing better to do (since cycling, TV, reading, writing this book and going out for coffee and cake, all take precedence over cooking). Tidying is so far down my to do list that it is practically off the page. I just don't see the point unless I have a guest coming round (usually my parents or someone I am dating). Even then, I only do it so that I do not have to listen to my parents' relentless ear bending about the mess, "Francesca, we are concerned about you. You live like a pig! It is not your fault; you are not well and you need help. You cannot see the mess because you live in it. If anyone else comes in here, they will die". This seems an overreaction to me, although their comments have been echoed by one or two men I have dated in the past. Thankfully, it never seems to put them off, suggesting it isn't as bad as my parents make it out to be; either that, or I have other amazing qualities that compensate for the mess.

I do tidy from time to time and I never let it get completely out of hand. However, it requires a certain mindset to allow my brain to engage in such an activity. I don't mind doing the dishes because it is repetitive and does not require much in the way of mental processing and decision making: fill the dishwasher and empty it. Everything has its place in a predetermined cupboard. In the cupboard to the right of the oven, the cups, which are all different sizes, are precariously placed one on top of another, resembling the Leaning Tower of Pisa – space utilisation at its best. The pots and pans are thrown into a pre-assigned cupboard on the left of the oven and the cutlery… well that funnily enough, lives in the cutlery drawer. Easy peasy. Well, you would think so wouldn't you? Despite my good intentions, I often find myself emptying half of the dishwasher before something distracts me and I wander off to do something else. You see, my problem is that I can only do one thing at a time and I really struggle to organise my mind in a way that allows for a structured method of tidying.

Say, for example, after half an hour's worth of deliberation and mental preparation, I consciously decide to hoover the living room. On my way to the hoover – which resides in the hall – I come across one of Oscar's jumpers on the floor. What do you think I do with it? I either step over it or put in on the radiator next to me in the living room just to move it out of the way. Why do I not put it in its rightful place you ask, in his bedroom? Before you say it, no, it is not because I am a lazy bitch… not on this occasion anyway. It is because my mind can only focus on one task at a time. If I put the jumper in Oscar's room, then I will be required to take a detour and the mental distraction will throw me off course and the hoovering will not get done. Something might get done, but it sure as hell won't be the hoovering.

Of course, I could just ask Oscar to tidy his own mess while I focus on the task in hand but that would require another skill I do not have: discipline. He would either ignore me or respond with an assertive, "No, I'm busy!" Then I would ask myself, *is it worth fighting over? No, not today!*

I find that the simplest of tasks require the greatest mental effort to undertake. I cannot tidy and clean an entire room in one session, without multiple breaks. It is even worse when I do not know where the items go – or even more likely – I know where the item should go, but there is an obstruction preventing access. Take for example, the pile of clothes that currently reside on my bedroom floor. I know they should go in my wardrobe, but there is no space for any more clothes. So, I consider my options… a) I could buy a new unit to store my clothes in – but why would I waste my money on "homey" stuff when I could spend my money on something more desirable such as a whole month of takeaways? Say I did opt for the least desirable option – to buy a new wardrobe – then I would need to choose one from a potentially huge selection… the mere thought of it is enough to stress me out. Okay, so what are my other options? Create space in the cupboard by throwing out clothes I no longer use – not possible. I would have so much difficulty deciding what to throw out, nothing would go. Having exhausted all other options, I decide to leave the pile of clothes on the floor for the time being, during which period the content of the pile changes on rotation (as I wear and wash my clothes) but the quantity of items remains the same. The same applies to Oscar's toys that currently reside in the open space in his bedroom – there is no more room under his bed to shove them out of the way. So instead, we leave them in a prominent location where we are forced to walk over them and hoover around them. Oh and those bloody Easter eggs on the kitchen unit – lack of space in my kitchen cupboards makes it impossible to store them out of sight. I cannot even contemplate the notion of emptying out the cupboards to create space. At least the eggs can be consumed, and their presence is therefore temporary. In fact, I will make a mental note to eat them during a pig out session tomorrow to finally get rid of them and create space on my kitchen worktop.

It's not all bad. I can focus on some tasks, albeit very specific tasks, for sustained periods at a time, and without much apparent effort: for example, studying for an exam or work-related activity. So why do I struggle to focus on simpler tasks? Perhaps it has something to do with my level of interest in the relevant subject. Probably not: I cannot say I ever enjoyed studying psychology or was particularly interested in the content of the course, yet I managed to get my degree (I will explain how this happened in the next chapter). A more likely explanation: the intensity of my focus is determined by the perceived importance of completing the task combined with the mental pressure imposed by me or other people. In addition, if the task contributes to or forms part of a larger overarching goal (usually related to my obsession) then my focus is infallible – to the point where I am in my own world and I lose track of time.

This is effective if the task is carried out in a structured setting, such as the workplace. At home, however, I am utterly useless. As I'm unable to manage my time efficiently, I struggle to form a routine and cannot develop a coherent structure to my day. I constantly find myself jumping from one thing to the next – busy all the time, yet, nothing gets done. Even now, I am sitting in my bedroom writing my book amid a chaotic mess, that I have no intention of tidying anytime soon. (Actually, that's not quite right: the intention is there, it just won't get done.) And yes, I have considered hiring a cleaner to offload some of the burden, but then I would be required to tidy before the cleaner comes which, in my mind, would defeat the purpose of hiring a cleaner in the first place. I have tried to change my approach to tidying without success. I have a busy life and I need to prioritise the tasks that offer the biggest reward (mentally) as well as those that have to be done in order to function successfully. In my opinion, tidying (and maintaining a tidy flat) requires maximum effort for minimum gain. I prefer to save my valuable, limited free time to complete the tasks that satisfy me most: and tidying is just not one of them.

Job For Life

Okay, so time for a quick recap. I had moved into the "new" flat with Oscar and was jobless and single. I was not happy with my situation I wanted a job for the sake of my sanity and a relationship to provide companionship and to assist with child rearing. Well, ideally, I would have loved to feel passion and excitement, but I was slowly coming to terms with the realisation that this might never happen, at least not with someone who was available (in other words, not married or otherwise involved). As for the job situation… well, we all know I had pretty much exhausted my options on that front. Some serious deliberation was required. I needed another goal to work towards, one that would challenge me mentally and help restore my confidence in my own ability but was realistic and achievable: an almost impossible task for someone who escapes real life by fantasising.

I momentarily considered the possibility of becoming a free rad; you know, one of those liberated, independent individuals with a zest for life who would say things like "I am young, free and single", "the world is my oyster" or "I will seize the moment". However, the reality of my mental limitations, financial difficulties, and parental responsibilities injected some much-needed perspective into this train of thought.

I had to formulate a low-level plan (bear in mind that my definition of low-level may differ from most) that was realistic, rewarding and most importantly, mentally feasible. I instantly found myself typing in the Google search bar: how to start your own business. This led onto another search… franchise for sale in my local area. I was excited when I saw a Costa franchise appear.

Now, who will lend me £250,000 to get started? No one in their right mind, next! I only require £30,000 to buy a popular Indian restaurant that is for sale – what a bargain! I could make a great return on my investment. Tell me more… where is it? Oh, I don't like that area. I would have to distance myself from my own restaurant and this would almost certainly put a spanner in the works… but perhaps I can employ someone to run the business on my behalf and I would work remotely, a guaranteed solution to my problem… No come on Francesca! BE REALISTIC! Think! I know, I will resurrect my studies, only this time with the Open University: a remote form of learning that will allow me to study at my own pace, in isolation and without the social pressures related to university life. As for the relationship, well there is plenty of time for that. One step at a time!

I was awarded a 75-point credit transfer towards my studies with the Open University (OU), the equivalent of approximately a year of full-time study. To give you a better sense of what this means, 360 points, split into various 15-, 30- and 60-point modules equates to a Bachelor of Science (honours) degree in Psychology with the OU. The 60-point modules are taught over a nine-month period and require an average of between 16 and 18 hours of study time per week. The 15- and 30-point modules require less study time per week than the 60-point module, which allows for simultaneous learning. As I could only feasibly study part-time, I worked out that it would take approximately five years to complete my degree, even with my credit transfer. Call me crazy – it is not even like I wanted to become a psychologist and I had not enjoyed studying psychology the first-time round – but this time was different. I was different. I was ready to prove to myself that I could and would succeed at something. While there may have been easier and more enjoyable ways of doing this, I had set my mind on this particular challenge and I was determined to see it through. I enrolled on the course that same day, and without hesitation.

Meanwhile, I also managed to secure a job. This was quite surprising really since I was visibly shaking during my interview. Thankfully, confidence and self-belief were not on their list of the must-have traits for a potential employee. I was offered a role as a receptionist for a small process control engineering company: a perfect opportunity to divert from the retail environment I had unwillingly become accustomed to. As an inexperienced receptionist with a habit of impulsively resigning from jobs without warning I was inevitably apprehensive about the strong possibility that I might let people down (including myself). It was a déjà vu moment as the obvious questions looped around my mind…

What if I am incompetent at the job? My colleagues will find out and, since they will not understand my anxieties, I am bound to panic and leave. How can I overcome this? I must hide my anxieties (something I have miserably failed to do in the past). I must refrain from crying in front of the boss and pretend to be normal. I will not allow my mental issues and insecurities to permeate my attitude in the workplace, not this time! But what if I feel uncomfortable in my new environment? That feeling will cross over to other areas of my life and could destroy everything I have built up over the past few months, including the way I feel content in the new flat. In this case, I will have to leave immediately.

Fortunately, the office was located in an area I was not accustomed to so it had no bearing on my previous life and the anxieties that accompanied it. This was not to say that my feelings about the location were a guarantee about the way I would feel in my new environment. However, it was a good start.

I tried to tell myself that, as much as I would have liked to control the outcome, there would many unknowns, so I had to stop dwelling on hypotheticals. Enough deliberation and on with the job, so to speak.

Fortunately, when it came to it, I immediately felt contented and secure in my new place of work: an instant, irreplaceable feeling that has remained intact for the duration of my employment to date. Frustratingly, I struggle to understand the reason why my current place of work gives me feelings of comfort and safety, when so many others have failed to do so. There is nothing specific I can pinpoint as the cause of my contentment, although there are several factors that I believe contribute to my feelings of safety: 1. It is located in an industrial estate and in neutral territory. Also, the route to and from work poses no threat to my mental well-being; 2. The building is big enough to prevent me from feeling claustrophobic but small enough to prevent my senses from being overwhelmed; 3. The number of employees ranges from 10 to 15. Any more than this would make me feel completely overwhelmed and out of my depth. I work alongside two older females, while the rest of the workforce are male. Again, this suits me since I seem to get on better with females who are much older than me, and I have also found that I often form better relationships with males.

The people in my workplace are quiet and reserved... well, everyone apart from me that is. My loud voice, impulsiveness, and open, emotional personality, possibly make me the exception to the rule. But I prefer to work with people who seem quiet and stable. It might be that I tend to get on better with this type of person because opposites attract. It must be said that there is something really endearing about a person who appears to be in control and who has a reliably stable personality, even when under extreme stress. By contrast, I can be both an introvert and extrovert, fluctuating from one to the other in different situations and with different people, and depending on my mood on any given day. This contributes to the fragility of my core identity, whatever that may be.

There were also some revelations about this new working

environment: "So, you are telling me that I can just get up from my desk, whenever I feel like, go and get a coffee and I don't need approval to do this?" *Unbelievable! So, wait, let me envisage this for a moment… I am sitting at my desk when suddenly, oh, I decide I want a coffee. I stop what I am doing, casually get up, walk over to the coffee machine (the fact we even have one is a novelty) pour a coffee, tea, or hot chocolate (yes we have options) without saying a word to anyone. If I am hungry, I can take a biscuit from the cupboard (without even hiding it) and go back to my desk to devour it, in plain sight. Incredible.*

Having worked in retail for most of my teenage life, I had become accustomed to a very different set of rules – whereby one was not allowed to leave the shop floor for any other reason other than for a quick toilet break, lunch break or to get something for a customer. Even then, someone had to cover your position until you returned. In that type of work environment, an unauthorised, sneaky coffee break would be deemed as incriminating behaviour, perhaps even a sackable offence. So, you will have to excuse me for thinking that the prospect of an "anytime" coffee break was the most amazing thing about my new job, so much so that I couldn't write about it without mentioning it.

The next big thing was the salary, which was significantly more than my previous salary of minimum wage + 13p per hour for the additional duties I undertook. Oh, and get this: I can actually wear whatever I want to work, within reason. (I don't think trainers and joggers would be an acceptable ensemble for a receptionist: or maybe it would be, I just haven't tried it.) If I want to wear a suit and look professional, fine! Equally, if I fancy a casual day, my normal day-to-day outfit of jeans and a suit jacket will suffice. Compare this to my previous experience of uniform etiquette: we were expected to procure the brand of clothing we were trying to sell, most of which were visually unappealing (patterns galore) and had to be tailored to fit: so the more relaxed dress code was most certainly a refreshing aspect of my new job.

Despite my inexperience, it turns out I was not so shabby as a receptionist. Within a short period of time, I had moved into a more demanding, but equally enjoyable role as a material coordinator. Well, this was the title I was given, but it is a procurement role that incorporates the coordination of materials as one of my responsibilities under a wider remit. The benefit of working for a small company – less competition and greater opportunity to undertake a wide range of tasks beyond one's original scope of work, thus contributing to the formation of that much sought after "well – rounded" individual.

By far, the biggest reward of working for a small company is that I am valued for my contribution, which never goes unnoticed. I cannot fathom why anyone would want to work somewhere where they are likely to be pigeonholed or seen as a number, as is often the case with larger companies. I would like to say it was my incredible, unique abilities that were the sole cause of my progression in the company, but I would be lying. In truth, I think it was more a case of being in the right place at the right time. My predecessor left the company just as I started, and as there was no one lined up to fill the position, it paved the way for me. And with increased responsibility, I received a pay rise, which far outweighed previous earnings, so it was an unexpected boost to my financial situation.

More importantly, my new role provided me with feelings of self-worth and self-satisfaction, which is imperative for my well-being. It felt like the job had been tailored to fit me and my particular skill set. I have to negotiate with suppliers to obtain good discounts and maximise profits, and I've found that the elusive "buzz" I get from buying and selling is not context-specific. Even when I do not stand to benefit directly from such financial gains, I get the same adrenaline rush from striking a good deal every time.

The method I use to complete tasks in the workplace is much like the approach I use at home: the jobs I deem to be important get done efficiently, while the insignificant jobs get ignored until I am under pressure to complete them. You might be wondering what the important jobs are. Raising quotes for clients, processing purchase orders, saving money and… and… well that's about it really. Due to their perceived level of importance in my mental hierarchy, it is not surprising that I consistently excel at these tasks under any circumstances.

The only exception to this is when I am extremely tired, stressed or anxious, to the point that I am crying inconsolably about something that others would perceive as irrational. The things that upset me would often appear as trivial issues to others. An example would be the relocation of the microwave from the kitchen near the entrance to the kitchen in the workshop. In my mind, it was an illogical move, one that was sure to disrupt my routine and would require a great deal of assimilation and mental adjustment to my existing construct of how the world should be. My colleague, and the person in charge of the big move, had of course, warned me in advance, giving me time to process the change before it occurred. However, for some reason, I had dismissed the idea. (Either that or I thought I would be able to cope with it.) So when it did happen, I was not prepared. I immediately became distressed and overwhelmed by my emotions and the only way to alleviate the pressure was through an emotional eruption, without consideration of those around me. Fortunately, my colleagues - who know me well and understand my condition - quietly waited for my meltdown to pass, then carried on as if nothing has happened: although I was admittedly embarrassed and ashamed immediately after.

Most of the mediocre tasks that are part of my job remit can be carried out without much difficulty and have become part of my daily routine. I am indifferent towards them but they can be done with relative ease, regardless of my mindset. These type of tasks include checking goods in and out and responding to client queries.

The most insignificant job, and by far the hardest to complete, is all the paperwork I am faced with. My desk at work is, to be frank, an utter mess, covered in all sorts, from delivery notes to yellow stickies with parts numbers for ordering, bills of materials, supplier quotes… you name it, it is all there. I would like to say that it is an organised mess but when my colleague is able to locate paperwork on my desk before I can, this would clearly be an inaccurate statement to make. As for tidying my desk, this is usually achieved organically when a colleague has requested a specific piece of paper that is embedded under a scattered pile of "stuff". Or, it might happen after numerous direct or subliminal attempts by the director to get me to tidy: "Wow, that's a messy desk" is usually enough to do it, but only if it has been mentioned repeatedly and I have had plenty of time to allow his request to sink in. Occasionally, my colleague just tidies my desk on my behalf – yes, this has happened, and more than once.

The project folders on the shelf behind me form a zig zag pattern in a limited, predefined space, with some folders deeply embedded at the back of the shelf and not immediately visible, and every second or third folder protruding its way out from the edge of the shelf (it's the only way to fit them all in without reorganising the entire unit). Of course, some of the projects are complete and the blue folders could be archived, which would create space on the shelf. However, I can only do this task if there is absolutely nothing else to do and I have a fully functioning mind, free of exhaustion, which is a rarity in my case.

My inbox as is messy as the physical desk I work at. I receive daily emails, warning me that my inbox is full and I may not be able to receive any more messages. In an attempt to rectify this, I move some of my emails into the correct folder (mostly ones from vendors), but then I come across a few ambiguous emails and, since am not sure where to file them, I decide instead to switch to a different and more enjoyable task, one that makes use of my procedural memory and does not require conscious decision making.

Cleaning in the workplace is, well… it does not happen. My colleagues usually know when I am in the office by the coffee spots on the floor, leaving a neat little trail through the workshop and the office, right up to the culprit's desk. I think it is less that I am clumsy, and more the fact that I do not clean up after myself that surprises people the most. In fact, just the other day, the director "had words" with me for putting dirty plates in the dishwasher – he even went as far as to retrieve them and leave them to soak in fairy liquid, for a wash before the wash. Of course, I questioned his motives. I question everything in the workplace; what is the point in having a dishwasher if you have to wash the dishes first? His response was both logical and acceptable: the muck on the plates could clog the dishwasher. Fair point… actually, this could explain why my dishes at home occasionally leave the dishwasher in the same state as they went in – note to self, check to see if dishwasher is clogged at nearest opportunity.

There is one other aspect of the job I dislike and avoid at all costs, and its name is… quality! This is an ongoing process that forms part of our quality management system (QMS) and is audited against the ISO 9001:2015 standard. The QMS, which is driven by risk-based thinking and strategic direction, identifies the processes, procedures and responsibilities for delivering on our aims, direction and future needs. Under the QMS, I am actively involved with the creation and revision of procurement-related work instructions and procedures, and I am required to demonstrate adherence to these procedures. While I understand the importance of quality in the workplace, and I am quite happy to follow procedures, I have a problem with the subjective nature of quality-defined tasks and procedures. In other words, one person's perception of best practice may vary considerably from someone else's point of view, but who is right and who is wrong? Arguably, there is no right or wrong answer and it is precisely this (the grey area) that frustrates me, resulting in a process of cyclical thoughts, helping me to produce a multitude of possible answers but preventing me from settling on the optimum one.

In terms of demonstrating adherence to procedures, I think, if you can justify your position, regardless of the outcome, then you will not be penalised for failing to do your job properly, and vice versa. I can only perform quality-related tasks for a limited time, (usually up to an hour maximum) and under very specific circumstances: it needs to be during the bust part of the boom and bust cycle – a way to describe the alternating phases of my economic growth and decline (in other words, when I have nothing else to do); I need to have slept well the night before and spent a few days building up to it, with the mindset of "I cannot possibly leave this any longer"; finally, it needs to be in preparation for an audit – this when the motivation stems from the idea that I would not like to be the one responsible for the failure of the audit.

Incidentally, at one point, I actually thought I would make a good auditor, to the point where I pursued my temporary goal by attending an internal auditor course. I wouldn't say it was a mistake as such – it is always good to learn and get a qualification under your belt, especially if it is applicable to your job. However, I struggled to understand, and still do to a huge extent, quality as a subject. I often perceive it differently from others and have found myself going round in circles arguing my case, on the basis that the person who shouts the loudest usually wins.

Of course, quality is imperative to the functioning of a company and, indeed, the whole supply chain. Yet I remain sceptical of it, or at least of certain aspects of it. I guess it is partly to do with how we incorporate it into our management system, but I find that it can create a lot of work that is often unnecessary and does nothing to improve the company's performance. Not surprisingly, it didn't take me long to realise that a career as an auditor was not for me.

Just as the location, the building and the people can have a positive influence on my mental state, they can also make me feel incredibly anxious. One experience stands out as poignant in my mind: I was asked by the company director to go on a training day that was being held at a client's premises. I wasn't bothered at first, perhaps even a little excited to get out of the office and learn something new. However, on the day, I felt entirely different. As soon as I arrived at my destination, I felt incredibly apprehensive. It was situated in a part of Aberdeen I had driven through on numerous occasions but where I had never stopped to assess my immediate environment. I immediately felt lost and out of control. As I sat in my car in the huge, deserted car park (meaning that it was deserted relative to its size), I tried desperately to create mental associations between the things that define me (mostly my flat and my work and my new environment), but it was hopeless. I was rapidly losing my sense of self and my confidence along with it. It is scary when I am in novel environments like this: I become numb with emotions, unable to feel positive emotions towards anything. The anxiety overrides all other emotions, making progress impossible.

After managing to leave my car and enter the building, I was overwhelmed and astonished by the vastness of my surroundings. It was like walking through an empty airport at night: everything seemed oversized in proportion to the number of people within. approached the large reception desk (one that I could hardly see over) on the right-hand side, perpendicular to the entrance. The lady behind the desk handed me a lanyard with the text VISITOR boldly plastered across the front, highlighting my status as a newbie to the area and confirming my identity as another number without a name. It didn't help that I was late (due to the school run), so when I entered the conference room, everyone was seated and the training was in full swing. I sat down in the nearest empty seat at the back of the room and spent the next hour or so half listening to the speaker, and half consumed by my thoughts (mostly about the people in the room). I wondered if the speaker was really that confident underneath all the bravado. Then I looked around the room. *Who are these strange people? I am glad I am not one of them, oh but wait – I am one of them.* My thought process was interrupted by the speaker who announced, "we will now be taking a short 15-minute break. Help yourself to bacon rolls and a drink".

As always, the mere mention of food was enough to capture my attention. It didn't take long for me to realise that what was supposed to be a break/stuff your face with free food session, was actually a mingle and make small talk with people you don't really know type of session. If I had been on my own work premises or had at least been forewarned about client expectations, I could have prepared myself, making it easier to engage with these strange people. However, I was unprepared, out of my comfort zone and suffering from a bout of severe anxiety, which made it almost impossible for me to hold a coherent conversation with someone I did not know. I did attempt to make small talk with a client who sat next to me and who had instigated the conversation. I found it really difficult to pretend to be interested and reciprocate the conversation with my own thoughts on the subject when: a) I was not interested and had no opinion on the subject; and b) I was aware that I was engaging in "forced" conversation that felt unnatural.

Perhaps, if there had been something to gain, like the possibility of winning a large contract, I could have performed in accordance with people's expectations. However, even if the possibility had arisen, my mind was geared towards it being a "training day" and a "training day" only. I lacked the experience and cognitive flexibility to interpret it as anything else.

I spent the remainder of the break observing, analysing others and forming first impressions based on their appearance, since this was all I had to go on. Most of the females appeared to be quite young: they had straightened hair and were dressed smartly in a tight dress, tights and heels. There was nothing striking about them to report, other than the fact that they were not my type of people, possibly because they appeared to be "too girly", meaning they would have a vastly different personality to me. The boys – oh jeez, don't even get me started. Most of them were wearing pointy shoes and a shirt so tight that you could see every contour of their body and their muscular arms, which looked desperate to rip through the material of their undersized shirt. In my opinion, a man who is vain, or at least appears this way, and feels the need to put their assets on display, is deeply unappealing. By contrast, someone with intelligence and an air of confidence (without showing off) trumps the stereotype of good looking every time. In fact, I would even go as far as to say that these "good looking" men are very insecure and are looking for reassurance by presenting themselves this way. Not that there is anything wrong with being good looking and insecure. I am sure a lot of girls (most even) find this type of man to be incredibly attractive: it's just not for me.

I am aware that I make judgements on people and sweeping generalisations based on first impressions. However, I think, whether we like to admit it or not, we all do this on a regular basis. In my opinion, it is not an inherently bad thing since it allows us to make sense of the world, navigate our environment effectively and affirm our identity. Imagine if we didn't pre-judge based on appearance? You would end up dating everyone on Tinder. (For the older generation who have no children and have been fortunate enough to avoid the era of dating apps, Tinder is a popular dating app, where you decide if you like someone based solely on their appearance, since there is little or nothing else to go on. For those of you who are familiar with the wonders of Tinder, I am sure you can relate to my thought process: *He has a nice smile. He seems like a nice person, swipe right (likey) or he has a picture of his torso and is only after one thing, swipe left (no likey).* Or if you are looking for a bad boy and just want sex, it's a swipe left for the "nice person" and right for the "asshole". This is possibly not my best example since I have indeed dated a lot of my fellow Tinderees, but hopefully you get my point. I am only saying all of this because I am worried that you, the reader, might be judging me for judging others… wait, of course you are, not just on this but everything I have written about in my book. It's only human.

At the end of the icebreaker, we were asked to reconvene in the presentation room. Everyone seemed more at ease, apart from me that is. I noticed that quite a few visitors were talking to their new "buddies" as they entered, with smiles and laughter filling the room as everyone took their seats. I couldn't help but wonder if I was the only person who felt out of place in this new, contrived environment that resembled a school day trip to an educational facility. *Are these people pretending to enjoy this training day to be polite, or are they actually getting something out of this?* It was just like being back at school: I struggled to pay attention to what was being said as there were so many other distractions in the room. Moreover, the speaker read out text that was also on a large screen, jumping between slides to demonstrate how the different elements interacted. This type of learning is, for me, confusing as it overstimulates my senses. I am much more likely to take in information if is conveyed though one channel only, slowly and in a comfortable environment (preferably without other people around).

Having said this, I did manage to pay attention when we reached the question and answer part at the end of the session. Let me explain why. The day before the event, we had had the opportunity to mail questions to the host. I guess I had been taking this invitation quite literally when I had asked, "Is it okay if I arrive approximately ten minutes late as I will be taking my son to school beforehand?". I had thought it was a little rude that no one had replied and had wondered if it would be an issue, which had only added to my feelings of apprehension beforehand.

When my question appeared at the bottom of the screen for all to read, I almost died. My palms began to sweat, and I became increasing shifty in my seat as the speaker read out the questions one by one, and my question inevitably moved its way up the screen. As the speaker read out my question, the room filled with laughter and heads turned to the likely candidate – it was obvious, since I was the only person who had been late. I have to say, it was not my finest moment: more of a "*ground please swallow me up*" scenario.

Following on from the presentation, we formed small groups and discussed different aspects of the training session – this was cringeworthy indeed. It was a small, nondescript room, next to the conference room. I envisaged an office desk with me working at it and immediately began to panic. *How am I ever going to leave my current job? What if circumstances that are beyond my control, force me to leave? I will not be able cope, as this experience has proven.*

I was feeling so insecure and out of place, I was desperate to escape and resume my own version of normal life. In groups of be-tween six and eight, we discussed a specific aspect of the training course, before moving onto the next table, on rotation. Being in close proximity to others, I had a better opportunity to assess in-dividual characters. There was one person, or possibly two people, I could imagine working with, both of whom were visitors to the premises. They were both male, average-looking, quietly confident, softly spoken and highly intelligent – just my type of people. It was strange to think that I worked with some of these people every day, albeit it remotely and via telephone and email exchange, but I felt no connection between them, my environment and my current place of work.

The realisation that I am mentally restricted in terms of what I can do and where I can go, began to sink in once again. I began to think about how isolated I am from the rest of society, and how I am dependent on my current routine and, on certain people. I im-agined how, hypothetically speaking, any changes to my current way of life would turn my life upside down, a frightening but also feasible prospect.

Once the event was over, I got into my car and immediately burst into tears. I felt completely overwhelmed and mentally ex-hausted from the whole experience and felt the need to release my emotions, in solitude. On the way home, I took a detour to include part of the route from my daily commute to and from work. In doing so, I had extended my journey quite significantly but at least that way I could disconnect the links I had formed between the anxie-ty-provoking area and my home life. By doing this, I could restore my previous levels of comfort and security. My final thought on the subject was: *God I hate these events but at least I now know what "post a question" and "take a break" mean, should I ever be required to go to another one.*

Having established that the location, building and people are the three main factors that determine my levels of anxiety, I wonder why these things have such an impact on my well-being when other people seem to breeze through life with minimal consideration of their environment. I also wonder if the three factors mentioned above are inextricably linked or if they are separate and distinct entities. For example, can I feel anxious when I am with a person who am usually comfortable with, but in an anxiety-provoking location and vice versa? The answer to this is undoubtedly yes, suggesting that one of these factors on its own is enough to evoke a negative emotional response.

I suspect this is where I differ from most neurotypical people, since I am led to believe that if most people feel anxiety, it would be based on the social interactions and social pressures, irrespective of the location. Or perhaps their mental state is impacted by their environment, but to a much lesser extent? The more I think about it, the more I realise that, in order to gain a better understanding of this, I should be focusing more on what goes on inside my head and less on the external, physically tangible aspects of this world, which only serve to act as a trigger for one of many predetermined emotional states.

In the context of my new job, the people and the building – a specific set of circumstances in which I navigate my way through the external environment – matched my prior expectations. This would explain why I instantly felt at ease in my new place of work and I did not have the anxieties encountered when a piece of the jigsaw does not fit and I am forced to change my environment to match my internal picture.

This is beginning to make sense.

On Reflection

always knew that I lived inside my own head but, even as I am writing this, I am struck by the intensity of it all – in a way, it is a poignant moment of self-revelation… a "holy shit, my life is an internal simulation constructed by my mind" kind of moment. This leaves me questioning how much of the world around us is based on preconceived notions and less on reality. For me, reality is fully embedded in the inner working of my wondrous mind. As a pattern thinker, who likes to feel in control and craves certainty in every situation, I create an internal, intrinsically bespoke model of how things should be. If the outcome (my actual perception as opposed to perceived perception) aligns with my initial expectations, then I feel in control and everything makes sense – just like finding the missing piece of a jigsaw to complete the picture. There is, however, little room for changes to my mental picture – how can you fit the wrong piece of the jigsaw without changing the entire picture?

As you may already have guessed, everything in my life is intense and extreme: I switch from being a pessimist and feeling depressed to being vivacious and over-optimistic, but never anything in between. One of my biggest strengths, my determination and passion to succeed is, for the most part, a reaction to failure and recurring anxieties I have experienced. Over the years, I have come to realise that what I had initially perceived as negative and limiting personality traits, if applied in the right context, become my strengths.

If only I could focus my obsessiveness and addictive personality on something healthy, such as sport or something career-related. This, coupled with my increasing resilience, determination and passion, would help me reach my goals and achieve self-defined success.

Shortly after I moved out of my parents' house and into the flat with Oscar, I suddenly felt the need to redeem myself for all of my mishaps: like the times I ran away, quite literally, from jobs, my studies, people, life! At the risk of sounding like I am bragging (well… am a bit), I obtained a 2.1 degree in psychology, all while working full-time and raising my son, who is now nine years old. I think I just scraped this mark, but to be honest – given my lack of commitment and suitability for the course – I was delighted with this result. It took me 11 years to complete but I got there in the end: I finally finished what I started. The studying did not end there either. Having established my newfound ability to persevere, I suddenly had a burning desire to achieve more and, specifically, to reach an optimum level of performance in the workplace.

The next logical step was to obtain a degree in mathematics and physics with the OU and train to become an engineer. Well, it seemed logical in my head anyway: I wanted to progress in the workplace, specifically, my current workplace. I had, inevitably, hit a career ceiling and, as I was not prepared to move to a different company, this seemed like the best… my only option. I signed up immediately and within nine months, I had successfully completed my first module in mathematics. I considered signing up for my next module but after weighing up my options and reassessing my goals, I decided to move on from the OU and undertake my studies with the Chartered Institute of Procurement and Supply. It seemed logical to advance in a subject that was relevant to my current role in the workplace. It would only take a couple of years to complete and, should the business grow, having this qualification would put me in good stead for progression to a more senior position, such as Procurement Manager. Finally, a job title like this would look good n my CV – not that this mattered really, since I had no plans to move on.

I have no idea how I manage to fit everything into my busy schedule. No, not true… I do know… I do it by prioritising the tasks I enjoy doing and by refraining from doing pretty much everything else. As for the tasks I do not like doing but have to do, I will do the bare minimum and only when it becomes a necessity. I have talked about my dislike for tidying, and how it is at the bottom of my list of priorities. Well, that is not strictly true. I would say studying is on a par, if not lower in the rankings. Possibly the only time my flat has been spotless is during study leave – anything to distract my mind from thoughts of the dreaded exam. Typically, I cram in all my studying into the final two weeks of study leave, during which my studies take the utmost priority (for once). A part of me wishes I were more organised – like one of those people who study all year round and subsequently, have very little to do before the exam… but then that wouldn't me, would it?

Instead, I have an innate predisposition to make my life as difficult as possible… planning would be far too easy, where is the fun in that? Well, that's my excuse anyway. The truth is, my brain will not allow for what it calls "premature studying". The "Don't think, Do" strategy as I like to call it, can only be applied once the mental pressure is sufficiently high to trigger a response. This is usually at the very last minute, when there is no time left to procrastinate, if success is to be considered a possibility.

I make it all sound too easy, don't I? You are probably thinking, she is one of those really annoying people who does nothing all year then somehow manages to wing it at exam time to achieve a pass…. and my answer to that is yes and no. It is true that the number of hours I spend studying, is significantly less than the recommended study time. But… and there is a big but… I pay for my lack of preparation in many ways. First and foremost, during the final week of study leave, I spend every waking minute (when my brain is functional) studying. I do not eat properly, I do not sleep properly and I sure as hell don't tidy properly, if at all. Then of course I have to use up all of my holidays from work in order to maximise the number of study hours available. The truth is, I don't like being on holiday, home or away – too much time to think and a lack of routine does not bode well for someone who overthinks and is incapable of having a structure to her day. "The Stress" my brain and body endure during the period building up to the exam, is by far my biggest punishment for being a last-minute type of person. Like an unwelcome and invisible enemy, it appears to creep up on me, lurking in the unconscious part of my brain, until… boom, it engulfs my entire being, to the point where I lose all control over my emotions.

I do not envy anyone who is in my physical presence at the precise moment when I explode: I have had several stress-related meltdowns in the workplace over the years and it is not a pleasant experience, for me or the person I use to vent my anger and frustration on. The signs of a pending meltdown are often subtle and ambiguous, but nevertheless present. I become fast talking (faster than normal), easily distracted, fidgety and more likely to pace back and forth. Internally, I begin to feel out of control, slightly disorientated and extremely irritable. I usually become very negative and pessimistic, questioning the meaning of life. *Is this it and then you die?* At the same time, I am bored and desperately seeking my next "buzz", to bring me back to life.

Frustratingly, at the time, and even after the event, I do not understand my emotions and struggle to pinpoint the trigger, which means it is extremely difficult to counteract my emotions with positive emotions and thus mitigate a meltdown. Distraction can help in such a scenario, but it has to be big, bold and dramatic – such as winning a lot of money, securing a large contract at work (where I am the responsible person for achieving this), someone I am obsessed with declaring their undying love for me, or even something negative such as the sudden death of someone I know. Since such a distraction is unlikely, fortunately in the latter example, there is little that can be done to resolve my negative mindset at this time.

Of course, I could try to eliminate all of the stressors, but then I would have to know what they are. And besides, once I have reached a certain level of awareness of my emotional state, it is often too late to switch to a positive mindset without the release of the build-up of negative emotions. Once I hit boiling point, my emotions are released, without apology or consideration for the way in which my behaviour impacts on others. During this time, my entire body is sweating profusely and I am crying inconsolably, with genuine tears pouring down my face. I feel worthless, miserable and extremely vulnerable. I want to be in control. I want to be strong and I don't want to be perceived as the type of person who cracks under pressure. So then, I ask the question: why do I not take myself off to a quiet room to release my emotions, instead of subjecting others to it? The answer to this, I believe, is because I am looking for support, for someone to acknowledge my pain and offer reassurance. I also crave a reaction, any reaction, whether it is positive or negative, to allow my mind-fuelled drama to tip over into reality.

Of course, I feel child-like and pathetic and, without any viable explanation for my outburst, I am unable to justify my position – it must seem like I am crying about nothing. Interestingly, I can cope well in situations where many people would crumble (the big, dramatic events) and a crying episode would be understandable to other people, if not expected. Yet I never have an explanation for my outburst, just a series of negative comments about why my life is so shit. *I cannot cope with this. I cannot be in a relationship since I cannot connect. I feel so unhappy and I do not know why. I am so stressed.* Over the next day or so, I become more subdued and a little embarrassed about my behaviour – trust me, I do not feel good about it. I question why I did it and perceive myself as pathetic and weak. I feel more vulnerable than ever and an overwhelming sense that *"I need to redeem myself for my actions".*

However, this, in turn, triggers a contrasting state of mind. It is at this point that I become strong and resilient, determined to build myself up again and prove my worth to myself and others. In what appears to be a sudden transformation, I become positive and begin to enjoy life again. *My life is good. I am capable of great things. I don't even want a boyfriend. In fact, why did I even say these things when they are not true?* Then, the same pattern follows… I build myself up, feel good and in control, ambitious and determined, until something happens… something that triggers my anxiety, causing an accumulation of negative emotions, and eventually an outburst.

And there I am back at square one, needing to climb all the way back up the emotional rollercoaster.

Taking Risks

Fifty pence profit on a £5 bet: simple! I had discovered a new money-making strategy and it appeared to be working. I am not one for betting when the odds are completely against me – if you do it frequently enough, you may get the odd lucky win but the majority of the time, you are inevitably going to lose. I have never understood this type of betting… Why do it this way when you can get the buzz from winning almost every time? Because most people do not get a buzz from making 50p on a £5 bet… but what if you establish a strategy that works, the accumulation of 50ps will surely add up. Also, if you increase the stake, then you are set to gain much more. My strategy was simple: bet during the second half of the football game on the predicted number of goals with odds of between 1:10 and 1:25. So for every pound put on, I had the potential to make between 4p and 10p profit. There are two things I did before settling on my bet: I searched for final score predictions from various football websites and I checked the stats during half time to see how many shots there had been on goal, both off and on target. This would influence my decision and the amount of risk I was prepared to take on each bet. I started small… betting £5 to start with, then gradually increasing my stakes by "reinvesting my profits", turning my £5 stake into £5.10, then £5.21 and so on. I could quite easily turn £5 into £10 in a day. It was of course hard work, but I loved it. Not only did I get a buzz from every win, but there was something extremely comforting in the process of betting. This is mainly due to its repetitive nature and the fact that it offers a distraction from my thoughts. When I see my profits increasing, I feel, to some extent, that I have control over the outcome and take comfort in knowing that I have single-handedly worked out a lucrative money-making strategy. This, in turn generates simultaneous feelings of excitement and contentment: feelings that cannot generally be generated by people. I have never perceived my approach to gambling as just a bit of fun: instead, it is a method for becoming a successful businesswoman.

It didn't take long for me to up the stakes and the amount of time I spent gambling. What started as a weekend session, soon turned into an evening and weekday affair. I started betting on Australian football games, which usually start around 7am or 8am, both on weekdays and at weekends. I was required to amend my strategy slightly with the Australian games since they scored more goals than their foreign counterparts. During the working week there was a huge selection of football games across the globe to choose from. I found myself betting on random teams from Harimau Muda v Petaling Jaya City to FC Tomtusk v CFC Tosno. I had never even heard of these teams, never mind their countries of origin. They could have been fabricated and I would have been none the wiser. Naturally, with such teams, the predictions to support my strategy were not available online. Instead, I relied solely on the in-game stats to support my decision on these games. In the evenings and weekends (midday through to 8pm) I bet on Premier League games, as well as all the top European teams. This provided me with a constant supply of daily fixes. Having established that I had a workable money-making strategy, I upped the stakes, quite significantly. I began to place £50 bets at a time and, at a ratio of 1:10, I was raking in £5 profit for every bet. There was the odd game that did not go as expected. This is where I relied heavily on the cash out option available, to limit the pain. Once, I reached £100, I withdrew £50 and started the process again. In my first week of doing this, I made £350 profit. I knew I was on to a winner.

Over a short time, I had developed an intense addiction – and my justification for it was its contribution to the enhancement of my well-being. The constant checking of my phone offered reassurance and comfort – especially when, as was often the case, I was running at a profit. However, during the odd occasion when I was running at a loss, I became increasingly frustrated and the phone checking process increased significantly, averaging between 400 and 500 times per day.

You see, the problem I have is that when I cash out and lose a huge percentage of my hard-earned profits, I want a quick fix, so I place riskier bets. If I lose all of my money (usually £50) I take a break (for a day or so) then I am straight back on it, and the only planned adjustment to my strategy is a psychological one: to remain calm and not allow my losses and subsequent emotional state to determine the decision-making process. *I must be patient, I am patient… No, I am not patient, I am impulsive and act on my emotions. How do I overcome this deficit in my personality? I know, I will stick with this, in the hope that, over time, my subconscious will, through trial and error, determine a pattern that allows me to become the self-made millionaire that I am destined to be.* Therefore, without any modification to my approach, I continue to make the same mistakes repeatedly, running on a profit for a few days then wiping out of all of gains when I become complacent or try to chase my losses. I tell myself it is worth it and that it is a constant challenge that I can thrive on without much in the way of losses. It is my hobby combined with my goal to determine the optimum strategy and become my own version of success… and never mind those who say gambling is a mug's game. *I am not like other people… with some perseverance and patience, I can… I will succeed where others have failed. Besides, even without the gains, as long as I stick to my motto or only lose what I can afford, then I am not hurting anyone and I can enjoy the process regardless of the outcome.*

This happened during a downturn in the oil and gas industry in which I worked. I was bored and frustrated and in need of an outlet for my emotions. Football betting was beginning to lose its appeal as I wasn't making money from it. I needed a new project, something to distract me from my thoughts. I considered putting all my mental energy towards studying, but this would have been a long term goal, so it would not suffice. I was looking for an instant fix, something that would really capture my attention and activate the reward system of my brain during this quiet period at work. Trading seemed like the next logical step for an entrepreneur in the making – it offered not only a focus, but also the possibility of making short term gains.

As I had little money to spare, I opted for CFDs – for those of you who are not familiar with this type of trading, it works with leverage, allowing you to make, and lose, more than you would with other type of trading. CFDs allow you to bet on whether the underlying value of the asset will go up or down, but you never actually own the asset. This can be dangerous as you can end up losing more money than you put in.

I started trading on the value of UK and US companies going up (Burberry, Tesla and Talk Talk to name a few). With a small number of positions open at any one time, my eggs were spread across multiple baskets, reducing the risk. After a couple of days with non-stop checking of my open positions, I was up by a modest amount: £5. A couple of days later and I was down £10... *bloody fluctuations in the market*. Every time I looked at the app (which was every few minutes while the market was open), I felt increasingly frustrated with seeing red numbers and minus signs. Even though my losses were small, and the technical data pointed to an imminent trend reversal in my favour, I was too agitated and impatient. My brain could not cope with the losses, so I had no option but to close the positions that were running at a loss. Even though I was now running at an overall loss, my brain was content to see blue numbers and plus signs against my open positions. This I could work with.

A week later, I had not only broken even, but I was up by £50. A day or so later, I was still up but only by £20… *screw this! Two bloody weeks and I have made £20 profit. This is not working for me. I need to find a new strategy for making money.* Comfortable in the knowledge that I was running at an overall profit, albeit a small one, I closed all my positions.

The following day, I woke up to the news of an alleged bribery scandal at *Petrofac* and more importantly, heard that their shares had slumped by almost 30%. *Great, an opportunity to make some money from short-term recovery.* I immediately bought some shares in Petrofac and, within a few short days, had made £200 profit. I quickly moved onto *Boeing* and a couple of other companies who were experiencing unexpected misfortunes – unethical, I know. I bought a couple of books on stocks and shares to try and make sense of the charts and all the technical jargon to assist with my decision-making processes. I'm not sure it really helped to be honest – mainly due to the unpredictable nature of the supply market.

The three most important pieces of information I obtained were: run with the gains and cut your losses; do not assume that an enduring downtrend (even when it is approaching a resistance line) will reverse direction simply because you think it has gone as low as it can go; and lastly, never chase your losses and do not risk what you cannot afford to lose.

Sounds easy, doesn't it? So with all of this in mind, I moved onto commodities and indices, which involves greater risk but higher levels of leverage. I was convinced I had the potential to make more money.

I started with oil and the FTSE. It didn't take me long to realise that such markets are volatile: they fluctuate massively and without warning, making it extremely difficult to make money. Work was quiet, so I had a good excuse to engage with my new hobby: day trading. I went through the commodities one by one, glancing at the charts to see how they had been behaving over the past week or so.

As a day trader, I was not interested in looking at the stocks' performance over the past year, other than to determine major resistance lines. Cocoa (you know the chocolate powder stuff) seemed to be behaving differently from other commodities: it was on a strong upward trend, seemingly passing through resistance lines with ease. Without researching the commodity, I immediately put all my money (around £500) on cocoa, betting that it would continue on its uptrend. I watched the candlestick chart and the value of the shares go up… and up.

An hour or so later, I was up £250. I was smiling from ear to ear as I ran through to the accountant's office to share the news about my gains. She was aware of my previous losses and, while she congratulated me, she also warned me to be careful. I wasn't really paying attention to what she was saying as I was too caught up in the excitement of my new money-making potential. I went for a quick coffee to supplement the endorphin party that was currently taking place in my head, then headed straight back to my desk to watch the money-making process in action. A message appeared on my screen, momentarily blocking the chart. It was an option to increase the leverage on my initial investment. I had to make a quick decision, to shoo the fly away to resume full screen viewing. I must have said yes, as within a few minutes, my profit had increased to £800. Another quick scoot around the workplace to share the good news and back to my desk to track the stock's movements. Half an hour later and I had lost £200 of my profits – *not to worry, there are going to be downward movements, as long as the overall trend is upwards then I am fine.* An hour later, I was at break-even point with all of my gains wiped out by one quick dip. I was not in the right emotional state to make an informed decision. I had gone from feeling elated to deflated within minutes. *Why didn't I take my money out when I was up £800? I could have controlled the outcome! Where do I go from here? Perhaps the increase in leverage was not a good idea, since I do not have enough in my account to cover the dips. I cannot dismiss the fact that just minutes ago, I was up £800. I need to recuperate my losses, so I will leave the position open.*

I nervously watched as the value of the shares went down… and down. Then, before I knew it, I didn't have enough margin to cover the drops and my position was about to be closed. I could not let this happen. I would lose close to £500 – my entire investment. So instead, I added £500 to my account, giving me a bit of breathing space before the anticipated resumption of the up-trend. Moments later, I had lost nearly all of that money too. My head felt tense and my body was shaking. I added another £2000 to my account, with the balance of my credit card now sitting at £3000 with only £2000 available. Moments later, I was down again and, in a last-ditch attempt to cover my losses, I added the remainder of my available funds. I felt sick as I watched my money wither away. I was willing, practically begging, that bloody candlestick to change direction and continue its upwards trend. A few minutes later and the unimaginable happened. I had lost it all: every single penny of my £5000 investment! Money I did not have!

I was less distressed about the money, and more about the frustration of getting it so wrong. I was so angry with myself for going against every trading principle I knew. *How… why did I let this happen? I have let my emotions win, again. Where is my self-control and why do I never learn from my mistakes! I do not have any self-control!*

To add injury to insult, I then watched as the value of shares finally made their way back up, but by then it was too late. My money was gone, and I had nothing else to put in. I had gone from feeling powerful and invincible to weak, fragile and self-loathing within an hour. I had failed on my mission, which, in turn, meant that I was a failure. This was a real challenge to my newfound resilience. I knew the road to recovery this time was going to be a long and turbulent one.

"I think you should see a psychologist". This was my mum's response having just found out that I had lost £5000 betting on CFDs. I couldn't breathe as I poured my heart out to her on the phone. "Francesca, you are looking at it the wrong way. You were never going to win. If it was really that simple, we would all do it". *I am not like normal people. I can do it. I just made a mistake. It all happened so quickly. I know I can learn from this. If only…, if only…* My mum explained that she thought I had a gambling addiction and urged me to access professional support. Although I heard the words she was saying, I was struggling to internalise them. Despite being able to acknowledge some of what she said, I still felt I had the ability to become a successful trader. From my research, I knew people made a living from it, so why couldn't I?

However, I was also experiencing guilt and shame. There was nothing I wanted more than to redeem myself. So, in a bid to improve the situation, even if only temporarily, I agreed with my mum and assured her I would seek help.

First Step To Diagnosis

Tell me about your Mother."

"She is crazy… not like crazy, crazy but just a bit nuts. She means well and would do anything for any of us, but she can be controlling (but with the best intentions) and her behaviour is often described by others as a bit odd. I think it's just because she gets bored, so she feels the need to create a drama. People love her though. She has great spirit and an amazing ability to get people talking and open up about their feelings".

The psychologist was trying to get a picture of my family to determine their influence on my development. The full story came tumbling out for the umpteenth time.

"Tell me again about your mother: how was she when you were growing up? Did anything traumatic happen in your childhood?" I knew where she was going with this, the good old nature versus nurture debate. She was trying to establish the extent to which the person I have become has been influenced by external factors, such as my upbringing.

"My mum suffered from premenstrual tension when we were growing up and she did fly off the handle from time to time. I guess t was quite scary, growing up in that environment".

"Did she ever hit you?"

Well yeah she smacked our bums if we were naughty. We did have the odd physical fight when I was growing up: she pulled my hair, I pulled her hair, kind of thing but she would never really hurt me".

I wanted to be as honest as possible and create a full picture of the family dynamics but at the same time, I didn't feel terribly comfortable with where she was going with this. After three, intense one-hour sessions, each a week apart, I had given what I believed to be a fairly accurate and comprehensive account of my life. The psychologist, who quite rightly had been liaising with her colleague between each session, concluded that I would benefit from further assessment. She explained that the doctor would have to request a referral, but she would provide the notes to form the basis of her written request.

I was asked to book an appointment with my doctor to discuss the referral process. It was standard practice really, a way for me to offer my permission to proceed with the request. "I warn you now" she said. It takes a while to hear back and most people don't get seen, unless you are you know, totally crazy" (this is what she said word for word, I kid you not). She then proceeded to go over my notes from the psychologist, upon my request. It started off sounding like a fairly accurate account of my life, reiterating everything I had said. That is until something extraordinary popped up that to me was fabricated at worst and inaccurate interpretation at best.. "she has been abused by her mother". The doctor read this part out casually, as if this was information I had divulged to the psychologist as a matter of fact. *Wow! What a strong statement to make after two meetings with me. Did I say something to make her think that? My poor mum, she will be mortified to hear this. I know she can be difficult at times but she loves me so much and would never abuse me. I mean, for goodness sake, she has been married to a social worker for the best part of 40 years. Surely, he would not have stayed with her all these years if she was an abuser?*

I did not correct the doctor since I did not see the point; she was simply reading the notes she had been provided with. Besides, it is possible that the psychologist added this nugget of fantastically inaccurate information to strengthen my case for a referral. As walked out of the doctor's practice, I reflected on the content of what had been said. *Did she really say that my mum abused me and only crazy people are successful in the referral process or did I imagine all of this? How bizarre!*

A couple of weeks later, I received a letter from the psychiatric hospital. I had an appointment with the senior nurse practitioner to discuss the possible benefits of psychotherapy to help me over-come my issues and incidentally confirm my status as a crazy person. Given my determination to unearth the workings of my own mind and understand why I am the way I am, psychotherapy seemed like the optimum method of support. Finally, it was a step forward in my endeavour to understand myself. I was hopeful about this time and believed I would get the answer I was looking for.

"I don't think you have a personality disorder and I am not sure psychotherapy would help you much – it is a group session and you would need to take time off work to attend". I agreed with this statement for two main reasons: group therapy would make me feel terribly uncomfortable and I was not prepared to take time off work and disrupt my routine, especially since I would be spending my valuable time discussing other people's problems instead of focus-ing on my own.

Following on from this, as she was summarising, she said, "One thought flitted through my mind. Don't be alarmed when I say this but you could be autistic. I am not saying you definitely are but there is a possibility". *Autistic, really? Interesting.* I can't say I had ever considered the possibility, but it was not surprising to hear either. The only person who had suggested this in the past was one of my dates, who had asked if I was autistic because of the way my eyes were darting around the room. *Why didn't I listen to him?* The nurse practitioner advised me that, unfortunately, the NHS only diagnose autism in children, so if I wanted to investigate further, I would have to go private (although I believe this may have changed recently there is now a route to referral for adults through the NHS). Then she asked the following question that surprised me, "Even if you are autistic, there is nothing you can do about it anyway… so do you really want to find out?" I was perplexed by this question. It was clearly biased towards the view that a diagnosis (the exact thing I had been looking for all my life) was not worth pursuing. I asked if there was anyone she could recommend, as I did want to pursue a diagnosis. She directed me back to my doctor.

My doctor's appointment could not come quick enough. I had researched the symptoms and completed an online diagnostic test for adults, in which my score was indicative of mild to moderate autism. I have always been sceptical of scale rating tests. However, my results supported the theory that I could be autistic and reassured me that I was on the right path to understanding myself better. The nurse's suggestion, coupled with the online test, gave me some hope of finding an answer and I finally felt I was on the right path to understanding myself better.

My doctor questioned what I had been told by the nurse and suggested that, based on his observations, he did not perceive me as having autistic traits: namely the lack of theory of mind (although I am not sure why he thought this since we had only had a brief conversation). After discussing the possible consequences of obtaining a definite diagnosis, my doctor provided me with the details of an autism specialist in my local area: John Forrester.

The Diagnosis

"I am confident that you have a diagnosis of autism spectrum disorder".

I cried as the words escaped his mouth. It happened almost instantaneously without the kind of mental processing that is usually required to facilitate one's emotional state. Finally, at the age of 32, I had the answer I had been searching for – that sought-after label which would inevitably help me, and others, to understand my thought processes and behaviour. I instantly felt complete, like every fragment of my entire being had come into alignment: the jigsaw pieces aimlessly floating around my mind, suddenly moved together as one, to form the perfect picture and thus to reaffirm my identity. I immediately accepted the diagnosis… more than that… I embraced it. After all, why would I question something that so eloquently described how my brain processes information, in a way I have never been able to comprehend, let alone verbalise?

I remember feeling mentally stronger, independent and self-assured as I left John's office after the diagnosis. It felt like I had accomplished something great. Finally, the person who had been hiding within me had been unearthed: the real me. I was buzzing, ecstatic and elated by the news. I felt like I had been given some sort of award.

It was the same sort of feeling I get when I win a bet or achieve something truly great. During the journey home, I kept replaying his words over and over "I am confident that you have autism" – relishing every moment of it in my mind. *Oh but wait…he didn't say that I definitely have autism. What if I don't have it after all? I will be so disappointed. I must obtain some clarity at my next session, just to be sure.*

I really hope he doesn't take this away from me. Just at this moment a song I liked started playing on the radio. The lyrics are 'oh she sweet but a psycho, a little bit psycho' and I remember thinking how fitting it was, in describing me: or at least it had been up until then

Life Post-Diagnosis

Nothing has changed and everything has changed since my diagnosis two years ago. Most of the external physicalities of my life are much the same as before: I am still working at the same engineering company, in the same role, in the same office, sitting at the same desk. I visit the same *Costa Coffee* every weekend, alternating between a child-friendly experience on those weekends when I have Oscar to a lengthier book-writing session followed by a coffee date on the weekends when Oscar is with his dad. I am still living in a messy flat: granted it's a different flat, but it's just as messy.

Moving flat is perhaps the most significant change I have made in recent years: it came from an autonomous, impulsive decision to uproot and move home, albeit it not far from my previous flat. The flat I bought is in the same block as the flat I rented, precisely one floor down. It was literally a case of moving my furniture downstairs in my pyjamas, in small manageable chunks. I had of course viewed a couple of flats in the village, both of which were on the main road, approximately 20 to 30 yards from where I currently live. However, the fear of the unknown prevented me from pursuing such an adventurous option: it was hard enough moving downstairs, not because of the actual move itself (honestly, my poor dad did most of the hard grafting) but because of the mental adjustments required for such a dramatic change in circumstances.

There was many a tearful-moment during the run up to the big move, and for days, possibly weeks after. Fortunately, there was a two-week overlap whereby I had the keys to my new flat but was still renting the flat above. During this time, I spent my days flitting between the two properties, thus allowing for a gradual change, making it that little bit more manageable. My parents joked that the only way of getting me to move was to lift me downstairs in hoist – fortunately, it did not come to this… close but not quite.

The layout of the two flats is almost identical. My parking space is right next to my old one and there is a shared entrance to the block of flats – minimal change, just how I like it. However, there was one small anomaly that required a great deal of adjustment – the newly purchased flat is at the end of the block and is exposed (not literally… as in, there is a wall there… but there is no adjoining property at the side of the flat). I find this lack of equilibrium frustrating. There should be something either side of the flat, offering both protection from the outside world and a sense of comfort. One other, rather significant difference between the two flats is that the rooms are the opposite way around: the living room is where the kitchen should be and the kitchen is where the living room should be. I would say the sensation this gives me is like walking on the ceiling, where everything is in reverse and not as it should be. Initially, this was extremely disorientating and required concerted effort to adjust, but I got there in the end.

I would say that the biggest changes to my life since diagnosis have come from within: in the wondrous workings of my mind. I now more readily accept my emotional states and I understand why I behave in certain ways. I am not saying it is easy, but just having the knowledge that there is a reason for my patterns of thought and actions is enough to give me comfort in navigating this life. I would also say that I have greater awareness of the triggers for my stress (such as unexpected change) and this makes it easier to manage them. Since my diagnosis, I no longer feel the need to push my boundaries to meet other's expectations of how I should behave. I find that by sticking to a routine that makes me feel comfortable, it reduces my anxiety, and makes it easier for me to cope with changes that I have no control over.

In terms of romantic relationships, there is nothing I would love more than to be in a well-established long-term relationship with someone I feel emotionally connected to. The problem I am faced with is that I am still unable to connect with anyone I have dated thus far, irrespective of the duration of our relationship. I often ask myself why I feel completely numb and void of emotions towards every man I date. Is it because I have autism? I am not capable of forming a romantic relationship or have I not yet met "the one"? Is there even such a thing as "the one" or do we have the mental capacity to fall in love with many people throughout our lives?

Can you believe that there are people in this world who can jump from one relationship to the next, like swapping out the old with the new, despite claiming to be in love with their previous partner? To say you love someone, and then finish with them, is unfathomable to me. I guess because I have never been in that situation, I cannot relate to it at all. However, surely if you love someone and you must if you have overtly declared your love to them) you would be invested in the relationship and do whatever it takes to make it work? Yet people end their relationships through choice, and not because their partner cheated on them or murdered someone. They make the conscious decision to cut all ties with the person with whom they have shared many years of their lives and fundamentally alter their existence in the process… just because they feel that "it is not working any more" – miraculous!

Over the past couple of years, the number of Costa dates I have arranged and participated in, amounts to well over 30, with a minimum of ten different men and, obviously, not all at the same time (although I have dated two people in one day and three over a weekend). I would say 90% of my dates turn into a second date – usually because the fundamentals are there and I am determined to see if feelings develop. Approximately 95% of the men I have dated have asked to meet me again and roughly 50% make it past the second date and onto the third. However, this is where difficulties arise, and I find it harder to commit any further. This is possibly because most of the men I meet are after one of two things: sex or the whole shebang (marriage, kids, commitment) with nothing in between.

My longest relationship since my diagnosis, lasted a whopping ten months. This could have been due to the fact that I was very honest with him and he was extremely accommodating. He did everything on my terms and never demanded anything in return. I liked everything about him: he was extremely attractive, genuine, financially stable, independent, caring, tentative, patient and so on. We got on very well, had the same interests and were similar in many ways. Yet, I struggled to commit emotionally.

Why can I not feel something, anything, for someone who clearly ticks all of my boxes? Am I not capable of developing romantic feelings for someone? Perhaps it is because I do not feel challenged by the person. It is possible that I perceive the person as my equal when, in fact, I am looking for my superior (or someone I perceive as my superior) who can look after and protect me, both sexually and mentally and in a dominating way.

I don't know what I am looking for, other than that elusive feeling – the same one I get when I achieve one of my goals. While companionship is nice, it is not enough for me to consider compromise and to risk making adjustments to my life in order to factor in another person. To invest my time and energy into someone else requires raw emotion as the sole driving force. He (the one) may be out there, then again, he may not… and while it would be nice to be in a stable, loving relationship and to experience genuine emotions that accompany this, I am just not sure that my brain is equipped for this type of relationship. I guess only time will tell.

I often wonder if an early diagnosis would have made things that little bit easier – from enhanced understanding of the workings of my mind to obtaining the right kind of support when needed, across multiple settings. Maybe I would have been better equipped to deal with life's trials and tribulations in the workplace, during my studies and at home. My family also feel that things could have been different if they had known earlier. Indeed, my mum is the first to admit, and I quote, "If I knew back then, what I know now, I would have handled things very differently. I would have been less forceful and more understanding towards Francesca's needs. As a mother it is both frustrating and heart-breaking to see your child retreat into themselves, unable to face the world. I could not just sit and watch from the sidelines as she threw away her degree and her jobs time and time again. I did not understand at the time: I thought she was being difficult and needed a good kick up the bum. So, I did what I thought was best. I know now that I was wrong".

Perhaps if my previous employers had been aware of my autistic traits, they would have been more understanding and supportive of my needs: particularly in relation to my difficulty with change and my need for structure and routine. Each and every time I left my job, on impulse and without warning, I felt ashamed and embarrassed afterwards. As I was unable to express my feelings, I did the only thing I could do: escape the situation by leaving my job. An early diagnosis would have made it easier for me to describe my symptoms (or at least given me the confidence to confide in my boss), and in turn, that might have prevented me jumping from job to job like a fleeting werewolf in the night.

During the times when I could not work, I did not seek emotional and financial support. Why? Because I felt my symptoms were not genuine, and I was not worthy of the support... and therein lies the problem; high functioning autism is a hidden disability. This is particularly the case for girls, who are often good at masking their autistic traits, as they learn to "mirror" neurotypical behaviour and appear to fit in. It is for this reason that many people get misdiagnosed or are not diagnosed until later, in adulthood. Indeed, many high-functioning autistic people live their entire lives without getting a diagnosis. I hope that after reading this, there might be even one person who is prompted to seek their own diagnosis and find clarity.

As I sit here now, in my kitchen with my laptop taking up the only available space on my breakfast bar (which suddenly seems far too small to accommodate everything), I ponder the true meaning of my diagnosis (mostly in terms of how it influences my perception of myself and society as a whole). Well, the truth is, there are people out there who think like me and who understand how I operate. This is both reassuring and something that reinforces my feelings of solidarity. Admittedly I have yet to meet one of those people, or at least I have yet to meet someone who has been officially diagnosed with autism. However, at the same time, I feel increasingly disconnected from the rest of society: my lifelong theory has been supported – my brain processes things differently from 99% of the population. My brain is different. I am different. I have always known this but now it holds a different meaning.

For the first time in my life, I have valuable insight into why I am different and, despite my limitations, I recognise my strengths (the passion and determination required to finish writing this book being one of them). The final diagnosis, 'High Functioning Autism', is so much more than just a label; it serves to enhance my self-worth and is crucial in defining who I am.

With this in mind, I can consider the once inconceivable possibility of maybe, just maybe, in time, removing the array of masks that have allowed me to fit in to a neurotypical-dominated world.

nd reveal my true self to the world… what a liberating and exciting hought!